THE NEW GRAB A PENCIL® BOOK OF WORD GAMES

RICHARD MANCHESTER

BRISTOL PARK BOOKS
NEW YORK

First Bristol Park Books edition published in 1999.

Bristol Park Books
A division of BBS Publishing Corporation
386 Park Avenue South
New York, NY 10016

Bristol Park Books is a registered trademark of BBS Publishing Corporation.

"Grab a Pencil" is a registered trademark of BBS Publishing Corporation.

Published by arrangement with Crosstown Publications.

ISBN: 0-88486-228-3

Printed in the United States of America.

Contents

Puzzles   1

Answers   81

Puzzles

KRISS KROSS

Fit the words for each Kriss Kross into their proper places in the diagram, using as clues the length of the words, and the letters linking them to other words. The words are listed alphabetically according to the number of letters. Some Kriss Krosses have a word entered into the diagram to help you get started. In this puzzle, to proceed, find the 5-letter word or phrase with "S" as its first letter.

3 LETTERS
Awe
Bow
One (*brother*)
Shy
Two (*sisters*)

4 LETTERS
Anne (*sister-in-law*)
Baby
Blue (*eyes*)
Five (*bridesmaids*)
Jane (*sister*)

Ruth (*grandmother*)
Slim

5 LETTERS
Crest
Crown
Laura (*niece*)
Maids
Raine (*stepmother*)
Sarah (*sister*)
Tiara
Wales

6 LETTERS
Castle
Curtsy
Edward (*brother-in-law*)
Jewels
London
Throne

7 LETTERS
Charles (*husband*)
"Duchess" (*childhood nickname*)

England
St. Paul's (*Cathedral where married*)
Stylish
Wedding
William (*son*)

10 LETTERS
Archbishop (*of Canterbury performed wedding ceremony*)
Coat of arms
Princess Di

Solution is on page 81

HOW WELL DO YOU FOLLOW DIRECTIONS?   by Eleanor Farina

If you follow all the directions given below carefully, you will change GOOD COMPANY into the name of something that provides such company. Be sure to work carefully, in order, step by step, for this puzzle is tricky. We have provided space for solving and have started you off by printing GOODCOMPANY, the direction given in step 1. See if you can solve this puzzle correctly on the first try. NOTE: "Y" is considered a consonant in this puzzle.   Solution is on page 81.

1. Print the words GOOD COMPANY, without a space between the words.

2. Move the 1st vowel from the right to the right of the 2nd consonant from the left.

3. Insert an R to the right of the 2nd vowel from the left.

4. Remove the 1st consonant from the left and replace it with an F.

5. Insert an I to the left of the 4th consonant from the right.

6. Remove the 3rd consonant from the right and replace it with an N.

7. Reverse the positions of the 1st and 2nd vowels from the right.

8. Move the 4th consonant from the right to the right of the 2nd vowel from the left.

9. Insert a C to the left of the 2nd vowel from the right.

10. Remove the first consonant from the right.

11. Exchange positions of the 3rd vowel from the left with the 5th consonant from the right.

12. Wherever two identical letters appear side by side, remove both letters.

GOODCOMPANY

_____

_____

_____

_____

_____

_____

_____

_____

_____

_____

_____

What's the item?

MAZE

by Larry Spuller

Beginning at the "S" on the left, see if you can find your way to the finish, "F," without crossing over any lines or retracing your path.

Solution is on page 81.

BOWL-A-SCORE CHALLENGER

In this bowling game, your "pins" are the groups of letters below. In order to score a "strike," you must make one 9-letter word from the 9 scrambled letters in each group. The starting letter for each "strike" word is given. If you can't get one word from the 9-letters, try for two words with no leftover letters. This will score as a "spare." However, to get a perfect score of 180 in this word-bowling game, you must form both a "strike" and a "spare" for each group of letters. NOTE: The letters in the "strike" and the "spare" words are not allowed to be in exactly the same order—some of the letters must be rearranged. EXAMPLE: OVER and BOARD would not qualify as a "spare" for the "strike" OVERBOARD; but ARBOR and DOVE would.

SCORING: Score 20 points for each "strike" and 10 points for each "spare."

WARNING: This game is really for experts! Only a word-bowling "genius" will score 180. The words we made are listed on page 81.

1.
N

I K

W G E

A A

N

Strike

A _____

Spare

_____

_____

2.
S

S S

E E L

C E

A

Strike

C _____

Spare

_____

_____

3.

K

C C

D H R

E E

E

Strike

C _____

Spare

_____

_____

4.

V

O T

I L N

E E

A

Strike

E _____

Spare

_____

_____

5.

U

T I

E F N

R R

U

Strike

F _____

Spare

_____

_____

6.

Y

S S

E I E

T M

R

Strike

M _____

Spare

_____

_____

HEXAGON HUNT

In the diagram of hexagons (six-sided figures) below there are 10 "special" hexagons. These 10 are special because the hexagons surrounding each of them contain numbers that are not only different from each other, but are also different from the number in the "special" center hexagon. We've started you off by drawing a circle in one of the 10 "special" hexagons. Now it's your job to find the other 9—can you find all in 4 minutes or less? NOTE: A hexagon may belong to more than one group, and a "special" hexagon may also be one of the surrounding hexagons in another "special" hexagon group.   Solution is on page 81.

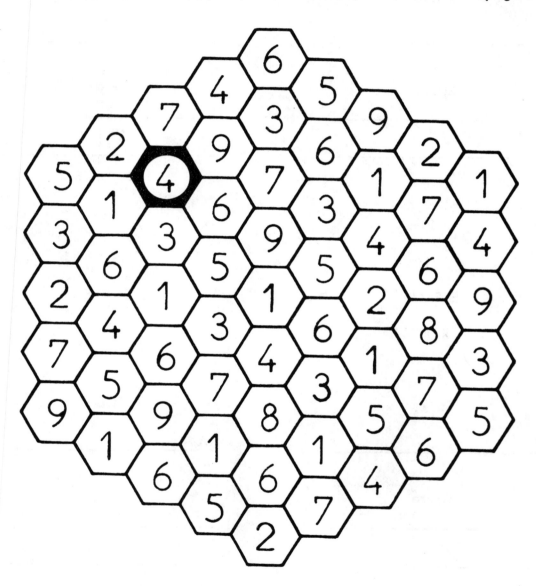

WORD MINE

Using only the letters in the phrase below, form as many 4- and 5-letter words as you can. You may use a letter more than once in a word ONLY if it appears more than once in the given phrase. Words beginning with a capital letter, foreign words, contractions, dialect, obsolete, archaic, and poetic words are not allowed. NOTE: Plurals ending in "s" and present-tense verbs ending in "s" are not allowed. We found 44 4-letter words, 11 of which are less frequently used, and 32 5-letter words, 14 of which are less frequently used. Our words are listed on page 81.

BASEBALL GAME

Your word list:

CHANGELINGS

Can you change the first word into the second word (in each set below) by changing only one letter at a time? Do not rearrange the order of the letters. Each change must result in a real, everyday word; and words beginning with a capital letter, slang, contractions, or obsolete words are not allowed. The number in parentheses indicates the number of changes we used for that Changeling.   Our answers are on page 82.

Example:	
TINY to BIRD	
(4 changes)	
TINY	
1. TIN<u>S</u>	
2. <u>B</u>INS	
3. BIN<u>D</u>	
4. BI<u>R</u>D	

1. B O L T to W O O L   (4 changes)

2. V O W S to W E D S   (4 changes)

3. H E R O to T E A M   (5 changes)

4. Q U I T to S T O P   (5 changes)

5. B E N D to L I M B   (6 changes)

TWO-WAY ANAGRAM GAME

The object of the Two-Way Anagram Game is to make words from the letters listed in each of the 18 horizontal and vertical rows in the diagram on the next page.

Each ACROSS word must start with the letter in front of each row and may be formed *only from letters found in that row.* Rearrange the letters, if you like, crossing them out as you use them.

Each DOWN word must start with the letter at the top of each column.

You need not begin by forming only ACROSS words, but may work in any order, solving ACROSS or DOWN, until all rows are finished. LETTERS MAY BE USED ONLY ONCE, so remember to cross out each letter as you use it; use only the unused letters that are left in a row or column to form your words.

The more letters used, the better your score. No proper nouns and no words of less than 3 letters are allowed.

Score 1 point for each letter in a formed word (including the beginning letter), and take away 5 points for each word you cannot form. WARNING: To get a perfect score, all the letters in the diagram must be used.

Average score: 77   Good score: 88   Perfect score: 99

Our solution is on page 82.

DIAGRAM

```
        B  U  T  R  O  D  F  I  H
   J    Y  S  O  E  L  A  W  L  T
   L    L  R  H  E  N  A  D  S  D
   E    O  E  P  I  X  T  R  R  A
   P    N  T  E  L  C  P  O  A  R
   V    U  O  C  E  L  T  T  I  I
   S    E  T  I  C  E  I  L  N  O
   A    D  U  K  L  C  T  E  I  B
   M    G  S  I  V  U  E  S  R  E
   C    E  P  H  E  E  R  Y  T  S
```

ACROSS			DOWN	
WORDS	**POINTS**		**WORDS**	**POINTS**
J_____	____		B_____	____
L_____	____		U_____	____
E_____	____		T_____	____
P_____	____		R_____	____
V_____	____		O_____	____
S_____	____		D_____	____
A_____	____		F_____	____
M_____	____		I_____	____
C_____	____		H_____	____

9

SPELLATHON

The idea of Spellathon is to spell as many 5- and 6-letter words as you can by moving along the connecting lines from one letter to another in the diagram below. Do not skip any letters. You may come back to a letter and use it more than once in the same word (as in "intent"); but do not stand on a letter, using it twice in direct succession (as in "inning"). Words beginning with a capital letter, foreign words, plurals, contractions, slang, obsolete, dialect, archaic, or poetic words are not allowed. We found 30 5-letter words, 11 of which are less frequently used, and 27 6-letter words, 7 of which are less frequently used. Our words are listed on page 82.

Your list of words:

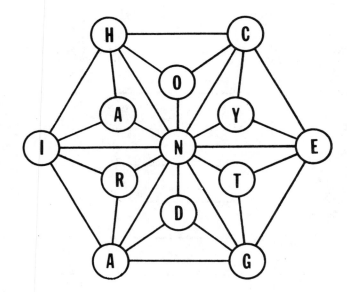

LADDERGRAM

by IRENE R. HAYES

First write the word that fits definition 1 into space 1. Then drop one letter and rearrange the remaining letters to form the answer to definition 2. Drop one more letter, rearrange, and get the answer to definition 3. Put the first dropped letter into the box to the left of space 1 and the other dropped letter into the box to the right of space 3. When you've correctly solved the puzzle, the dropped letters in the boxes on the left and those on the right, when read down, will spell out related words.

Solution is on page 82.

1. Definitions

1. Zebra marking

2. Makes an effort

3. Ascend

4. Rental documents

5. Bargain-day events

6. Not as much

7. Capital city of France

8. Tears (apart)

9. Small taste

10. Palace

11. No longer fresh, as bread

12. Make airtight

13. Trustworthy

14. A rolling "one" gathers no moss

15. Short letter

1	2	3	
4	5	6	
7	8	9	
10	11	12	
13	14	15	

ANACROSTIC

by JACQUELINE E. MATHEWS

1. In the Words column, answer all the definitions you can; only a few words are enough to begin solving. The fun of solving Anacrostics is working back and forth from Words column to Diagram and finally completing both. 2. Enter each letter from the Words column into its correspondingly numbered box in the Diagram, as we have done with Word A. 3. Work back and forth from Words column to Diagram, as words begin to form. A black square in the Diagram indicates the end of a word. The completed Diagram will contain a quotation; the initial letters of the completed Words column will spell the name of the author of the quote and the title of the work from which it was taken. Word List (answers to Definitions), page 82. Quotation, page 82.

Definitions										Words		

A. Crooked ....
B **E** **N** **T**
86　9　82　119

B. Immediately: 2 wds. ....
78　22　43　99　68　10　18　105　120

C. Little Rock's State ....
35　117　97　66　2　34　84　13

D. Bit of information ....
69　7　55　80

E. Current-events report ....
42　3　62　108

F. Disney character: 2 wds. ....
29　116　61　88　75　40　52　107　76　49

G. Mistake ....
77　25　39　58　67

H. Wilder; less sensible ....
36　89　26　32　83　100　20

I. Unprejudiced: hyph. wd. ....
38　6　79　48　94　71　56　12　17　111

J. Huck Finn's craft ....
46　112　70　104

K. In the past: 3 wds. ....
95　114　63　21　15　106　31　59　28

L. Buy (a meal) for .... $\overline{98}$ $\overline{11}$ $\overline{53}$ $\overline{74}$ $\overline{92}$

M. Truman's successor .... $\overline{33}$ $\overline{73}$ $\overline{91}$ $\overline{60}$ $\overline{23}$ $\overline{115}$ $\overline{45}$ $\overline{14}$ $\overline{65}$ $\overline{102}$

N. Soil .... $\overline{90}$ $\overline{41}$ $\overline{96}$ $\overline{44}$

O. — to mind, recall .... $\overline{8}$ $\overline{16}$ $\overline{118}$ $\overline{110}$ $\overline{4}$

P. Special event .... $\overline{19}$ $\overline{37}$ $\overline{72}$ $\overline{109}$ $\overline{103}$ $\overline{101}$ $\overline{81}$ $\overline{51}$

Q. Nancy —, detective of fiction ... $\overline{27}$ $\overline{64}$ $\overline{87}$ $\overline{57}$

R. Bulgaria's neighbor .... $\overline{5}$ $\overline{113}$ $\overline{24}$ $\overline{93}$ $\overline{30}$ $\overline{85}$ $\overline{47}$ $\overline{54}$ $\overline{1}$ $\overline{50}$

DIAGRAM

1 R	2 C	■	3 E	4 O	5 R	6 I	7 D	■	8 O	9 A (E)
10 B	11 L	12 I	13 C	■	14 M	15 K	16 O	17 I	■	18 B	19 P	20 H	21 K	■
22 B	23 M	■	24 R	25 G	26 H	27 Q	28 K	29 F	■	30 R	31 K	32 H	33 M	34 C
■	35 C	36 H	37 P	38 I	39 G	40 F	41 N	42 E	43 B	■	44 N	45 M	■	46 J
47 R	48 I	49 F	■	50 R	51 P	52 F	■	53 L	54 R	55 D	56 I	■	57 Q	58 G
59 K	60 M	61 F	■	62 E	63 K	64 Q	65 M	■	66 C	67 G	68 B	69 D	70 J	71 I
72 P	73 M	74 L	75 F	■	76 F	77 G	78 B	79 I	80 D	81 P	82 A (N)	83 H	84 C	85 R
86 A (B)	87 Q	88 F	89 H	90 N	91 M	■	92 L	93 R	■	94 I	95 K	96 N	97 C
98 L	99 B	100 H	101 P	102 M	■	103 P	104 J	105 B	106 K	107 F	108 E	■	109 P
110 O	111 I	■	112 J	113 R	114 K	115 M	116 F	117 C	118 O	119 A (T)	120 B	■

13

QUOTATION PUZZLES

To solve, fit the letters in each column of a puzzle into the boxes directly above them in order to form words. When you are through, you will discover a quotation by reading across the boxes in the diagram. The letters may or may not go into the boxes in the same order in which they are given; it is up to you to decide which letter goes into which box above it. Once a letter is used, cross it off the bottom half of the diagram and do not use it again. A black square indicates the end of a word.

The quotations are on page 82.

1.

V	B	A	T	S	A	O	A	T	L	O	I	L	A	M	O
E	E	R	T	K	O	N	U	L	O	T	C	N	I	S	B
I	R		C	H		F		T	O		F	E	I	L	I
	T		I			A		L						T	

2.

S	Y	L	G	H	A	L	Y	P	C	T	E	N	I	A
N	I	N	C	R	O	N	E	R	A	R	N	T	E	S
	O		E		I	O	D		T	A	A		T	A
	A		Y		T	P	D		A	H	E			

TREE TRIVIA

Trees provide us with fruit, shade, and lumber, among many other things. Here's your chance to test your knowledge of one of nature's most useful and beautiful resources.   Answers are on page 83.

1. How can one tell the age of a tree?

2. The leaves of what tree were used as clothing by Adam and Eve?

3. What country has the maple leaf as its national emblem?

4. True or False:
   a) Americans use more than 40 million Christmas trees annually.
   b) The maximum age of any tree is about 2,000 years.
   c) Deciduous trees are those which do not shed their leaves.
   d) In one year, the average person in the U.S. uses wood equivalent to one ton of lumber.
   e) The modern use of plastics has greatly reduced the need for wood and other tree products.

5. By what name was the itinerant tree-planter John Chapman better known?

6. During what month is Arbor Day celebrated?

7. What kind of tree:
   a) is the tallest in the world?
   b) was used to build King Solomon's temple?
   c) is George Washington said to have chopped down?
   d) did Longfellow's "village smithy" stand under?
   e) was Sir Isaac Newton sitting under, according to legend, when he discovered the law of gravity?

8. What State is known as the "Palmetto State"?
   a) South Carolina   b) Georgia   c) Alabama

9. Can you name a kind of tree beginning with each of the letters in the word FOREST?

10. Joyce Kilmer's famous poem "Trees" begins: "I think that I shall never see . . ." Can you complete the line?

CRYPTOQUIZZES

A Cryptoquiz is a list of related words put into a simple code. Spot familiar words by their "patterns" of repeated or double letters, and

1. HORSE-DRAWN
Example: surrey

Z S L L O

I J N D L U

G K L P F

I M K L N A P K A U

U K F I P X   A K Z

A K E E D K L N

M K F Q N X

Z S A R Z P K E Q

I S J R O

A U K E D P M

2. FURNITURE STYLES
Example: Louis XV

I Q G V Z E Q L R

D E J R G K

X E Z I Q R G Q L M

J H X Q E J

G Z M Z R Q L M

G K Q X X J R S L M J

K J X X M J B K Q V J

J L E M N

L H J E Q G L R

S L R Q O K   H Z S J E R

CRYPTOQUIZZES

you can solve the rest, for if G stands for M in one word, it will be the same throughout the list. A new code is used for each Cryptoquiz.

Answers are on page 83.

3. "C" THE COUNTRIES
Example: Congo

I K L S

I Q N T C

I V F O K H

I S X C O Y Y P

I S P S Z S

I Q N P S

I Y H U S   O N I S

I Y T Y X L N S

I S F C   R C O Z C

I Q S Z

4. THE LONE RANGER
Example: white hat

Q Z I Q Z

Y F C E J   V C X J

X A F L G N   Y K F F G Q X

"M A - B Z   X A F L G N,

    C T C B !"

Q G O C X   N C I P G N

Z F S   T G X Q

P Z Z S   P K B X

"J G V Z   X C Y G"

E C K P M Q   Z K Q F C T X

LOGIC PROBLEM

CONVERTING TO A CO-OP
by Evelyn B. Rosenthal

Mr. Erskine and four other men live on different floors of an apartment building that is being converted to a cooperative. Under the conversion plan, senior citizens and handicapped persons cannot be evicted, but all others have to buy their apartments or move out. From the following clues, can you find the full name of each man (one is Val), his floor, and how he is affected by the conversion?

1. The tenant who is buying his apartment lives two floors lower than Tom and two floors higher than Will.

2. Sam lives on a lower floor than Roy and on a higher floor than Mr. Ackley.

3. Mr. Daley, who is not Sam, lives on the third floor.

4. Mr. Collins lives two floors above the tenant who plans to move, who lives three floors below Tom.

5. Will is not either of the men who cannot be evicted.

6. The tenant who is still undecided about whether to buy or move is not Mr. Ackley.

7. Mr. Bradford lives on a higher floor than the only senior citizen among the five.

Solution is on page 83.

Use the chart below to help sort the information given in the clues. Use an X to indicate "no" for an eliminated possibility and a dot to indicate "yes" for a confirmed conclusion. Once you enter a definite "yes" (dot), put an X for "no" in the rest of the boxes in each row and column that contains the dot.

	Roy	Sam	Tom	Val	Will	Buy	Move	Senior Citizen	Handi.	Undec.	Floor				
Ackley															
Bradford															
Collins															
Daley															
Erskine															
Floor															
Buy															
Move															
Senior Citizen															
Handi.															
Undec.															

CROSS SUMS

In Cross Sums puzzles, the numbers in the black squares refer to the sum of the digits which you are to fill into the empty squares. The number ABOVE the diagonal line refers to the empty squares directly to the RIGHT of that number. A number BELOW the diagonal line refers to the empty squares directly BELOW that number.

No zeros are used here, only the digits one through nine. An important point: A digit cannot appear more than once in any particular digit combination. We have shaded one area in the diagram. If you need help starting the puzzle, the digit combination that goes into this shaded area is given on page 83. Solution is on page 83.

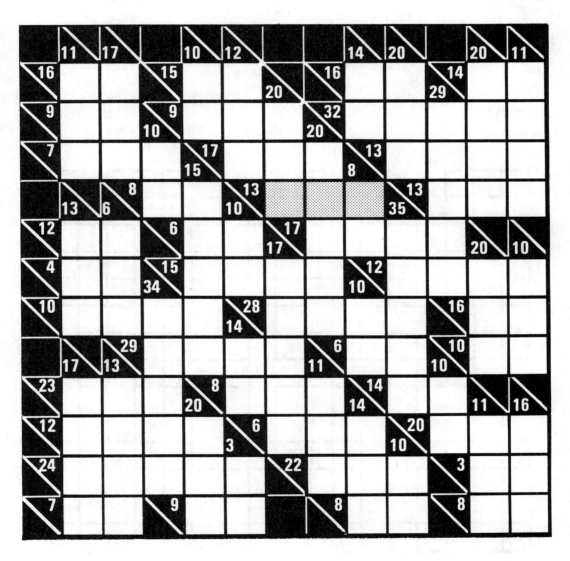

KRISS KROSS

Expert solving time for this Kriss Kross, with the word SASS already entered in the diagram, is 26 minutes. Your solving time:

3 LETTERS
Ese
Ess
Mrs.
Sam
Set
She
Sis
Son
Spa
Spy
Sun
Use

4 LETTERS
Asea

Asia
Bass
Cass
Espy
Esta
Hash
Hasp
Husk
Ides
Isle
Sack
Sane
Sass
Says
Sent

Serb
Silo
Size
Spot
Star
Stop
Task
Tsar

5 LETTERS
Amass
Asset
Class
Dress
Essay

Moist
Pasha
Passé
Pasta
Seats
Sepia
Slaps
Snips
Stack
Swiss
Tasty
Tests
Tosca
Tryst
Years

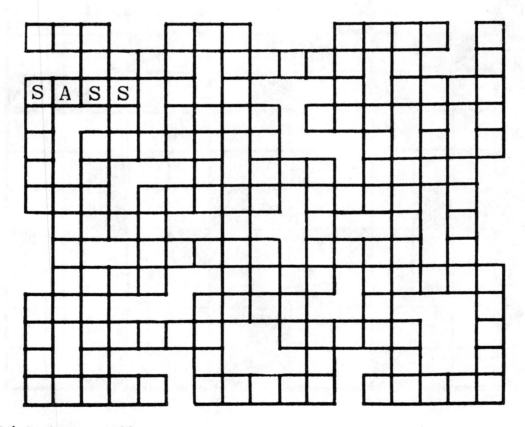

Solution is on page 83.

ARROW MAZE

Starting at the S (start) and following the arrow leading out of that S, see if you can find your way to F (finish) in five minutes or less. When you reach a square that contains an arrow, you MUST follow the direction of that arrow, and continue in that direction through the empty boxes until you come to the next arrow. You may not simply go through a square that contains an arrow, and you may not change directions until you hit an arrow that tells you you may do so. When you reach a square that has two arrows, you may choose either direction. In this maze, it's okay to cross your own path.   Solution is on page 84.

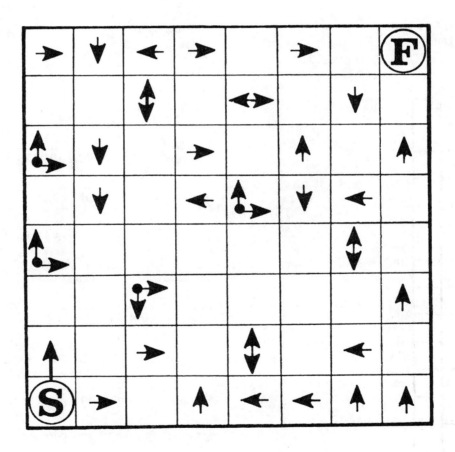

ANACROSTIC
by RONALD SCHOENLEBER

1. In the Words column, answer all the definitions you can; only a few words are enough to begin solving. The fun of solving Anacrostics is working back and forth from Words column to Diagram and finally completing both. 2. Enter each letter from the Words column into its correspondingly numbered box in the Diagram, as we have done with Word A. 3. Work back and forth from Words column to Diagram, as words begin to form. A black square in the Diagram indicates the end of a word. The completed Diagram will contain a quotation; the initial letters of the completed Words column will spell the name of the author of the quote and the title of the work from which it was taken. Word List (answers to Definitions), page 84. Quotation, page 84.

Definitions

Words

A. Young Girl Scout ....
B	R	O	W	N	I	E
120	110	44	75	2	22	89

B. Immature; silly ....
61	38	16	103	125	51	78	4

C. Earnest attempt; effort ....
86	26	46	113	95	64	10	130

D. It heralds the break of day ....
108	35	97	9	87	65	50

E. Foamier ....
101	31	48	20	79	63	5	119

F. Lingered longer than originally intended ....
53	25	128	90	1	115	66

G. Monotonous; boring ....
112	102	94	6	77	36	129

H. Oval, purple-skinned fruit eaten as a vegetable .....
18	122	49	81	114	33	70	88

I. Faithfulness; allegiance ......
41	69	96	127	85	56	8

J. Associate (oneself); join ......
7	91	21	80	68	57	123	28	109

K. Final offer or demand ....
83	23	12	54	106	67	117	98	34

L. — as a lamb, not violent ...... $\overline{71}$ $\overline{14}$ $\overline{55}$ $\overline{111}$ $\overline{40}$ $\overline{126}$

M. Fireplug .... $\overline{29}$ $\overline{42}$ $\overline{74}$ $\overline{59}$ $\overline{104}$ $\overline{19}$ $\overline{116}$

N. Alleviate, as pain; comfort ..... $\overline{37}$ $\overline{76}$ $\overline{27}$ $\overline{131}$ $\overline{13}$ $\overline{62}$

O. Without prior preparation or ...
study; impromptu $\overline{93}$ $\overline{32}$ $\overline{11}$ $\overline{100}$ $\overline{72}$ $\overline{124}$ $\overline{47}$

P. Informal bulletin issued to .....
subscribers $\overline{133}$ $\overline{121}$ $\overline{43}$ $\overline{15}$ $\overline{84}$ $\overline{30}$ $\overline{99}$ $\overline{3}$ $\overline{60}$ $\overline{92}$

Q. Servile follower .... $\overline{24}$ $\overline{132}$ $\overline{58}$ $\overline{107}$ $\overline{45}$ $\overline{73}$

R. Wrap up; embrace .... $\overline{118}$ $\overline{52}$ $\overline{82}$ $\overline{39}$ $\overline{17}$ $\overline{105}$

DIAGRAM

1 F	2 A *N*		3 P	4 B	5 E		6 G	7 J	8 I	9 D			10 C	11 O	
12 K	13 N	14 L		15 P	16 B	17 R	18 H	19 M	20 E		21 J	22 A *I*	23 K	24 Q
	25 F	26 C	27 N	28 J	29 M	30 P	31 E		32 O	33 H	34 K	35 D	36 G	37 N
	38 B	39 R	40 L	41 I	42 M	43 P	44 A *O*	45 Q	46 C		47 O	48 E	49 H	
50 D	51 B	52 R —		53 F	54 K	55 L —		56 I	57 J	58 Q		59 M	60 P	61 B
62 N	63 E	64 C	65 D	66 F		67 K		68 J	69 I	70 H	71 L		72 O	73 Q
74 M		75 A *W*	76 N	77 G	78 B	79 E	80 J	81 H	82 R	83 K	84 P		85 I	86 C
87 D	88 H	89 A *E*	90 F		91 J	92 P	93 O	94 G		95 C		96 I	97 D	98 K
99 P	100 O	101 E	102 G	103 B		104 M	105 R	106 K	107 Q	108 D	109 J	110 A *R*		111 L
112 G	113 C		114 H	115 F	116 M	117 K	118 R	119 E		120 A *B*	121 P	122 H	123 J	124 O
	125 B	126 L	127 I	128 F		129 G	130 C		131 N	132 Q	133 P		

WORD ARITHMETIC

These are simply long-division problems in which letters are substituted for the numbers 0 to 9. Solve each problem, writing every letter, as you discover its value, above the correct number on the line provided. When you are finished, the letters will spell out a word or phrase.

Answers are on page 84.

1.

`0 1 2 3 4 5 6 7 8 9`

```
                    A W E
        WOES | T W E N T Y
                A Y A S
                A O N T
                W O E S
                  Y Y T Y
                  L F E S
                  W W F Y
```

2.

`0 1 2 3 4 5 6 7 8 9`

```
                    O H M
        BOOT | M A M M O T H
                M O M P I
                T T M T
                B O O T
                I H O S H
                R O H H B
                M P A P
```

3.

`0 1 2 3 4 5 6 7 8 9`

```
                    C O W L
        CLUB | D O U B L E D
                L W C B
                U W N B L
                U D W O B
                C B K L E
                U N C W B
                U B D E D
                N D L B
                U B U D
```

4.

`0 1 2 3 4 5 6 7 8 9`

```
                    B A N
        SIR | B R O G A N
              G S L L
              A O G A
              R D R L
              N D A N
              O S R L
              S O N
```

JIGSAW LOGIC

Fit the ten jigsaw pieces into the grid so that each line across and down contains all six symbols, shown to the left of the grid, once each. The symbols in the grid should not be moved or changed. The pieces can be turned in any direction, but do not change their shape. For a starting help, see page 84 for the location of the shape marked by the arrow.

Solution is on page 84.

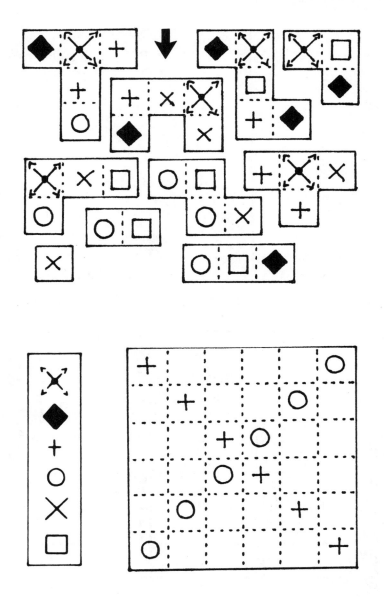

LADDERGRAM

See directions on page 11.

Definitions

1. Fifth tire
2. Pod vegetables
3. Baltic is one
4. The same
5. Tahoe or Huron
6. Huge deer
7. Black birds
8. Trap
9. Close by
10. Pester playfully
11. Sunrise direction
12. Had a snack
13. Holders for film
14. Otherwise
15. Bandleader Brown
16. Stupid mistakes : slang
17. Sleep noisily
18. Pete —, baseball superstar
19. Zsa Zsa or Eva
20. Boast
21. Cake (of soap)
22. Throbs
23. Wagers
24. Abbreviation in a recipe
25. Begin to grow, as young plants
26. Rains cats and dogs
27. Clam chowder, for one

1	2	3	
4	5	6	
7	8	9	
10	11	12	
13	14	15	
16	17	18	
19	20	21	
22	23	24	
25	26	27	

Solution is on page 84.

LOGIC PROBLEM

PARENT-TEACHER NIGHT   by Ellen K. Rodehorst

During a recent Parent-Teacher Night at a small elementary school, Mrs. Wilson and three other parents discussed their children's progress with their teachers; the four children are in first, second, third, and fifth grades. The four teachers include Ms. King, and one child's first name is Jon. From the clues below, can you determine each child's full name, grade, and teacher?

1. Sarah, who is not the Brady child, is two grades ahead of the Sullivan child.

2. Ms. Black told Mrs. Carter that her child should have no trouble advancing to Ms. Peck's class next year.

3. Holly, who is not Mr. Turner's student, liked school more last year, when she was in Ms. Peck's class.

4. Michael is not the second-grade pupil.

Use the chart below to help sort the information given in the clues. Use an X to indicate "no" for an eliminated possibility and a dot to indicate "yes" for a confirmed conclusion. Once you enter a definite "yes" (dot), put an X for "no" in the rest of the boxes in each row and column that contains the dot. Solution is on page 84.

	Wilson	Brady	Carter	Sullivan	1	2	3	5	King	Black	Peck	Turner
Jon												
Sarah												
Holly												
Michael												
King												
Black												
Peck												
Turner												
1												
2												
3												
5												

LETTER COUNT

The idea of Letter Count is to form everyday English words, Kriss Kross style, in the diagram on the next page using only the letters given in the graph above it. Each letter in the graph has a numerical value which is determined by adding together the number of both the row and column in which the letter is found. For example, D is in the fourth row and third column and therefore has a numerical value of 7; one of the E's has a value of 3, since it is in the first row and second column (there are other E's and they will have different numerical values). In entering letters into this diagram, the number value of each letter must match the number of its square in the diagram. We have started you off by filling in the word "APT" and crossing off in the graph the A with a value of 8, the P with a value of 6, and the T with a value of 12. To solve, try out the various letter-number possibilities for the combinations of squares in the diagram until you have determined the correct letters and words. Here's a suggestion: fill in the letters with the highest and lowest numerical values first. It's a good idea to cross off each letter as you use it, since each letter is used once and only once. NOTE: There are no plurals or words beginning with a capital letter in the puzzle.

Solution is on page 85.

1 2 3 4 5 6 7 8

	1	2	3	4	5	6	7	8
1	T	E	N	R	E	T	M	T
2	A	R	A	O	R	Y	R	E
3	E	G	T	M	L	A	O	R
4	L	R	D	T	C	R	E	T
5	P	L	C	D	S	W	H	E
6	E	A	E	A	T	E	A	U

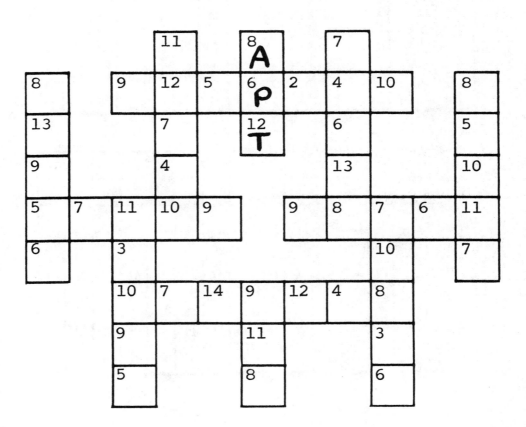

QUOTATION PUZZLES

To solve, fit the letters in each column of a puzzle into the boxes directly above them in order to form words. When you are through, you will discover a quotation by reading across the boxes in the diagram. The letters may or may not go into the boxes in the same order in which they are given; it is up to you to decide which letter goes into which box above it. Once a letter is used, cross it off the bottom half of the diagram and do not use it again. A black square indicates the end of a word.

The quotations are on page 85.

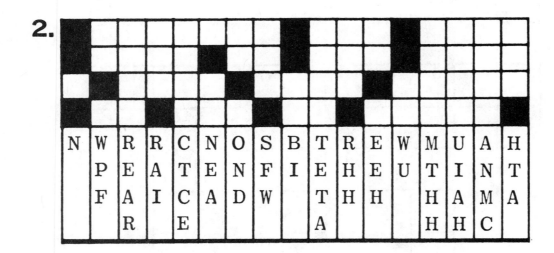

WORD WHEEL

Starting with the letter "L" at the arrow, see how many everyday words of three or more letters you can find in the wheel below. Always go in a CLOCKWISE direction and don't skip over any letters. Words nestle within other words, so look carefully. Where some words end, other words begin. Abbreviations, contractions, foreign, slang, poetic words, or words beginning with a capital letter are not allowed. Remember: Look only for words that are three letters or more in length.

NOTE: You cannot count the same word twice. You may, however, count each different FORM of a word. For example, if you saw the letters C, A, R, E, D, you would score five words: CAR, CARE, CARED, ARE, RED. In this Word Wheel, words ending in "S" are not allowed.

Our list of 34 words is on page 85.

Your list of words:

CRYPTIC MATH

Each of the nine letters below stands for one of the numbers one through nine, but no two letters stand for the same number. Using the five clues, can you deduce the number represented by each letter?

Solution and explanation are on page 85.

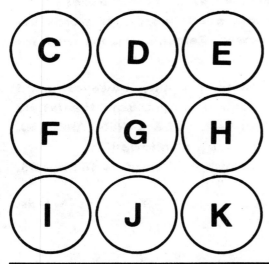

1. D is an even number.

2. $E + K = 6$, and $E \times E = K$.

3. $J = 8$.

4. $H = I \times I$.

5. G is smaller than C; C is smaller than D.

MOVIE THEME MATCH

Listed in the left-hand column below are a number of well-known movies. On the right is a brief description of the plot or other prominent element of each movie. See how many you can match up.

Answers are on page 85.

1. Greystoke: The Legend of Tarzan

2. The Best Years of Our Lives

3. Christine

4. Footloose

5. Thunderball

6. PT 109

7. Shane

8. Beverly Hills Cop

a. An evil 1958 Plymouth

b. The new boy in town wants to dance

c. Sean Connery as 007

d. An English lord is raised in the jungle

e. Three WWII veterans try to adjust to civilian life

f. Eddie Murphy wears a Mumford High T-shirt

g. Alan Ladd as an ex-gunfighter

h. JFK's World War II exploits

BUILD SCORE

The object of Build Score is to form 5-letter words for the highest possible score. You do this as follows: In the diagram below, one letter of each word to be formed is given. Use the letters to the left of the diagram to form your words and score yourself according to the number value preceding each line of letters. You may use a letter as many times as you wish in forming your words. Don't forget to count the letter given in each line as part of your score. For example: On the first line, you would score 30 points for JUMBO, 31 points for GLOBE, 35 points for ALIBI, or even a higher score for another word (other words are possible). Solve each line in this way. Words beginning with a capital letter, foreign words, slang, contractions, obsolete, poetic and dialect words, and plurals are not allowed.   Our score of 405 is shown on page 85.

POINTS	LETTERS
10	B K U
9	A P S
8	G L V
7	C Q
6	H M W
5	D R T
4	I N X
3	E Y
2	J O
1	F Z

DIAGRAM

1			B	
2			U	
3			I	
4			L	
5			D	
6		S		
7		C		
8		O		
9		R		
10		E		

LADDERGRAM

See directions on page 11.

Definitions

1. Oven-bake, as meat
2. Kind; type
3. Decay
4. Pays attention (to)
5. Good way to be in a library
6. Face wrinkles
7. Uncles' wives
8. Salad fish
9. Mr. Cole of music
10. Frightened
11. Jack, trey, queen, king, etc.
12. Disfiguring mark
13. Shriek; yell
14. Measures of land
15. Autos
16. Baked —, Boston dish
17. Sensible
18. Baltic or Mediterranean
19. Commandment, "Thou — not steal"
20. Derby, bonnet, etc.
21. Cigar residue
22. Wander off
23. Paving or roofing substances
24. Actor Carney

1	2	3	
4	5	6	
7	8	9	
10	11	12	
13	14	15	
16	17	18	
19	20	21	
22	23	24	

Solution is on page 85.

SPELLATHON

The idea of Spellathon is to spell as many 5-letter words as you can by moving along the connecting lines from one letter to another in the diagram below. Do not skip any letters. You may come back to a letter and use it twice in the same word (as in "rarer"); but do not stand on a letter, using it twice in direct succession (as in "error"). Words beginning with a capital letter, foreign words, plurals, contractions, slang, obsolete, dialect, archaic, or poetic words are not allowed. Our list of 36 words, 8 of which are less frequently or rarely used, is on page 85.

Your list of words:

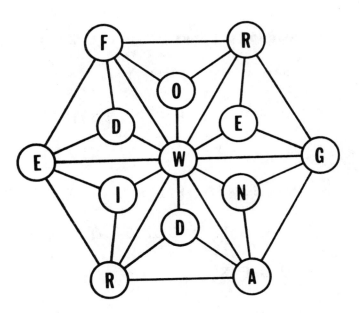

CRYPTOGRAMS

These Cryptograms are all in simple substitution codes—another letter of the alphabet is substituted for the right letter. THE WHITE DOG might be written RNS LNGRS MPI, R being used for T, N for H, S for E, etc. By noticing the frequency of certain letters (e, t, a, o, i, and n are usually the most frequently used letters in English) and by looking for patterns of letter repetition in the words, you should be able to "break" each code. Every Cryptogram is in a different code.

1. **ABC's**   L V   C N B I   P L V G   L D   J M   N F G M

   E N N A ,   K N M ' Q   E N I G   V N P A D   E C

   I G J K L M U   N B Q   N V   L Q .

2. **The good old days**   Y P B C Z ' F   D P F Y C U J V C

   I P D F V F Y F   P L   W R I C U U V D J

   Z R F Y R W B C Z ' F   E W V I R F .

3. **Work pays off**   E L S G ,   E L N N G E E   Q E

   E O G G X ,   C L X   Q X E   E G N S G X   Q E

   E O G F X .

4. **A good game**   D X R Q N I   W B F I N T A

   T N F B B I   Q P X G   D X G   Y X   W F A A

   Y D N   W C R Q .

CRYPTOGRAMS

5. Memories K B G L Y D Z J Y   J G   L M X   E J D X

L M Y L   H X S B I X G   Y K Q   H B R Z M

X C Z X G   E H B S   L M X   Z B B C   B D C

C Y Q G .

6. A healthy mixture B V   V T U R W   A N V E   W C G

T G X   F T B G   V N   P T U R   T

Z N G X R F Q C K   T G X   X R K B J E V Q C K

F T B G A N Z .

7. A good lesson X L R V   I L H V M Q T O H D

Z Y M M S X   C V   D R L Z O Y T V Q   Y X   Y

I Y H L .

8. Happy thoughts S V C R J X V   C   A V X R T L

H T X   O X V C Q   R J Z R Q C L I V   Z B   Q M V

R Q X V Q I M   T H   M D R   D S C O D L C Q D T L .

9. Holidays F J L A   T N R J X W Y N H   J X X N L K

V N H X W Y N   V J F W R A   T N S L W Z L

E N R K   W L   Z R K   E Z F N H X N J K .

Solutions are on page 85.

ANACROSTIC

by RONALD SCHOENLEBER

1. In the Words column, answer all the definitions you can; only a few words are enough to begin solving. The fun of solving Anacrostics is working back and forth from Words column to Diagram and finally completing both. 2. Enter each letter from the Words column into its correspondingly numbered box in the Diagram, as we have done with Word A. 3. Work back and forth from Words column to Diagram, as words begin to form. A black square in the Diagram indicates the end of a word. The completed Diagram will contain a quotation; the initial letters of the completed Words column will spell the name of the author of the quote and the title of the work from which it was taken. Word List (answers to Definitions), page 86. Quotations, page 86.

Definitions

Words

A. "Man" from outer space ......
M A R T I A N
24 84 11 109 50 67 58

B. Penetrate: 2 wds. ....
59 45 131 7 72 88 102 23 34 121

C. Time after which a person .... must be indoors
30 125 117 83 3 101

D. Regulates, as a watch ....
132 14 124 39 62 29 95

E. Mingle among (prominent .... people): 3 wds.
37 75 66 122 134 110 54 18

82 27 94 47 6

F. Poe's, "The — Heart": .... hyph. wd.
127 112 22 140 71 57 44 9

G. Containers ....
86 12 69 79 99 49 114

H. 24 hours ago ....
123 73 20 46 60 136 100 35 8

I. In theory; perfectly ....
138 76 116 89 13 104 26

J. No way!: 2 wds. ....
106 129 120 31 63 74 52 91 41

81 2 21

38

K. Progeny .... $\overline{16}$ $\overline{119}$ $\overline{43}$ $\overline{141}$ $\overline{96}$ $\overline{61}$ $\overline{108}$ $\overline{33}$ $\overline{77}$

L. Manicurist's tool: 2 wds. ...... $\overline{51}$ $\overline{19}$ $\overline{115}$ $\overline{133}$ $\overline{42}$ $\overline{4}$ $\overline{68}$ $\overline{87}$

M. Dam and reservoir on .... $\overline{78}$ $\overline{25}$ $\overline{111}$ $\overline{40}$ $\overline{93}$ $\overline{1}$ $\overline{64}$ $\overline{130}$ $\overline{15}$
the Rio Grande, in New
Mexico: 2 wds.

$\overline{103}$ $\overline{53}$ $\overline{85}$ $\overline{135}$

N. Cosmetic preparation: 2 wds. .. $\overline{70}$ $\overline{17}$ $\overline{55}$ $\overline{126}$ $\overline{80}$ $\overline{28}$ $\overline{105}$ $\overline{38}$ $\overline{92}$

O. Gather into a whole or mass; .. $\overline{113}$ $\overline{36}$ $\overline{5}$ $\overline{139}$ $\overline{48}$ $\overline{128}$ $\overline{65}$ $\overline{107}$ $\overline{97}$
total

P. Invading swiftly and rapidly ... $\overline{98}$ $\overline{10}$ $\overline{118}$ $\overline{56}$ $\overline{32}$ $\overline{90}$ $\overline{137}$

DIAGRAM

1 M	2 J		3 C	4 L	5 O	6 E	7 B	—			
8 H	9 F	10 P	11 A	—	12 G	13 I	14 D		15 M	16 K	17 N		18 E	19 L
20 H		21 J	22 F	23 B	24 A	25 M	26 I		27 E	28 N	29 D	30 C	31 J	32 P
33 K	34 B		35 H		36 O	37 E	38 N	39 D	40 M		41 J	42 L		43 K
44 F	45 B	46 H	47 E	48 O	49 G	50 A	51 L	52 J		53 M	54 E	55 N		56 P
57 F	58 A	59 B	60 H	61 K	62 D		63 J	64 M		65 O		66 E	67 A	68 L
69 G	70 N	71 F		72 B	73 H		74 J	75 E	76 I	77 K	78 M	79 G		80 N
81 J	82 E		83 C	84 A	85 M	86 G	87 L	88 B		89 I	90 P	91 J		92 N
93 M	94 E	95 D	96 K	97 O	98 P	99 G	100H		101C	102B	103M	104I	105N	106J
107O		108K	109A		110E	111M		112F	113O	114G	115L	116I	117C	
118P	119K		120J	121B	122E	123H		124D	125C	126N	127F		128O	129J
130M		131B	132D	133L	134E	135M	136H		137P	138I	139O	140F	141K	

39

FOURTH OF JULY MAZE

by Larry Spuller

See if you can find your way from one end of the bundle of firecrackers to the other without crossing over any lines or retracing your path. Try to get from start to finish in less than two minutes—before the fireworks go off!

Solution is on page 86.

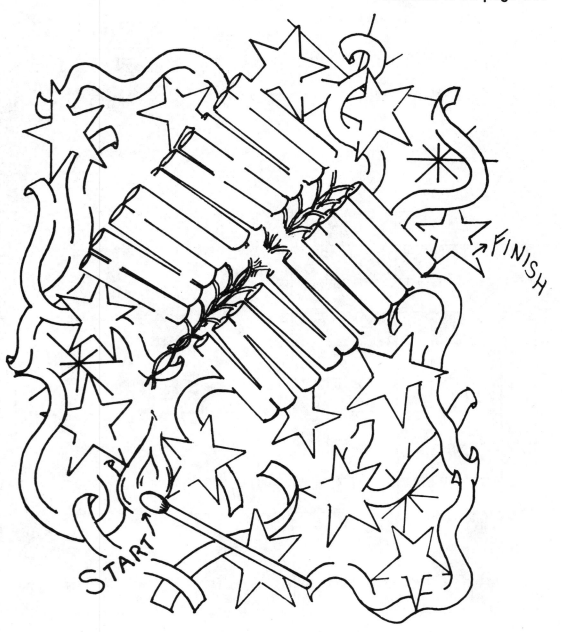

KRISS KROSS

This Kriss Kross is not that tough, but it makes a good warm-up for the Kriss Krosses on the following pages. All the J's have been entered in the diagram as a help.

3 LETTERS
Jam
Jeb
Jed
Jet
Jim
Joe

4 LETTERS
Jack
Jail
Jess
Jest
Joel
Joke
Joss (*Chinese idol*)

Juju (*West African magic charm*)
Juno (*Roman goddess*)

5 LETTERS
Jaunt
Jeers
Jelly
Jolly
Joust
Julie
Jupon (*jacket or tunic formerly worn with armor*)

6 LETTERS
Jaycee
Jersey
Jetsam
Jingle
Jocose
Jungle
Junior

7 LETTERS
Jacobin (*Fr. Dominican friar*)
Jealous
Jejunum
Jocelyn
Joinder

Jonquil
Jubilee
Jujitsu (*Japanese wrestling*)
Jupiter

8 LETTERS
Jehovist (*unidentified Old Testament writer*)
Jetliner
Jettison
Jongleur (*wandering minstrel*)

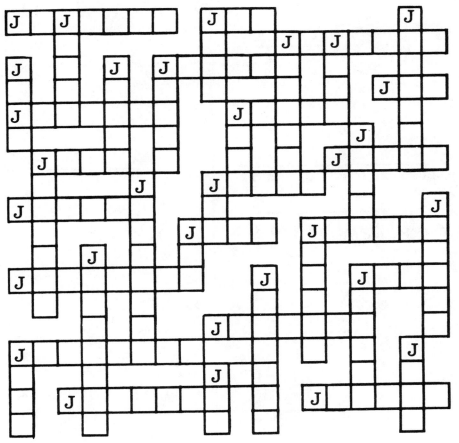

Solution is on page 86

WORD ARITHMETIC

These are simply long-division problems in which letters are substituted
for the numbers 0 to 9. Solve each problem, writing every letter, as you
discover its value, above the correct number on the line provided. When
you are finished, the letters will spell out a word or phrase.

Answers are on page 86.

1.
```
    0 1 2 3 4 5 6 7 8 9
    _____
                 N O R
I O N | M O D E R N
        M R R N
        _____
          R Z M R
          R N E H
          _____
            A N R N
            A R D H
            _____
              R M N
```

2.
```
    0 1 2 3 4 5 6 7 8 9
    _____
                   A L E
L U T E | T E N D E D
          T T Q Q
          _____
            A I T E
            L U T E
            _____
            L U O O D
            L I Q A L
            _____
              L D Q L
```

3.
```
    0 1 2 3 4 5 6 7 8 9
    _____
                 A P E
S T O P | E A S T E R N
          T T P B
          _____
          A P S E R
          A S U O P
          _____
            P S E N
            S T O P
            _____
              S N U
```

4.
```
    0 1 2 3 4 5 6 7 8 9
    _____
                 R A N
M O P E | P O L I T E
          M O P E
          _____
          R T R N T
          I T E N
          _____
          M T N A E
          A N M E A
          _____
            A P M I
```

CROSS SUMS

In Cross Sums puzzles, the numbers in the black squares refer to the sum of the digits which you are to fill into the empty squares. The number ABOVE the diagonal line refers to the empty squares directly to the RIGHT of that number. A number BELOW the diagonal line refers to the empty squares directly BELOW that number.

No zeros are used here, only the digits one through nine. An important point: A digit cannot appear more than once in any particular digit combination. We have shaded one area in the diagram. If you need help starting the puzzle, the digit combination that goes into this shaded area is given on page 86. Solution is on page 86.

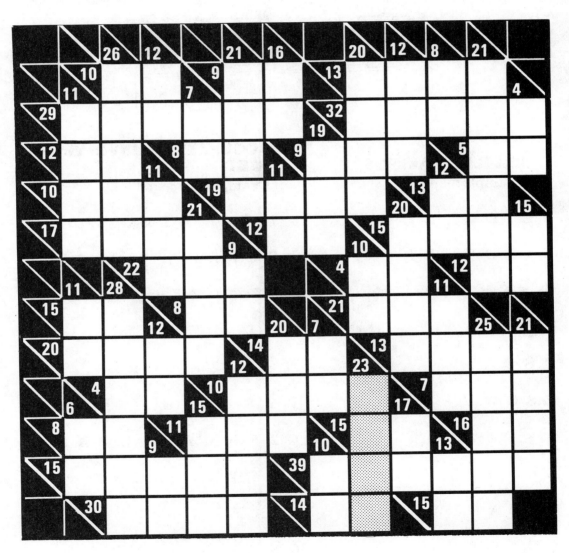

CRYPTOQUIZZES

A Cryptoquiz is a list of related words put into a simple code. Spot familiar words by their "patterns" of repeated or double letters, and

1. JEWELRY MAKINGS
Example: silver

O L I W

H I C E F G K R

W F C R L G W V

U L A C I

H S C A I V

P S C W V

A K P F S V

E K A T K L F V S

S R S A C I W V

O C A G S E V

2. OCCUPATIONS INVOLVING FOOD
Example: grocers

L M Y A V R Z E

L S G R Z E

T S Z O R Z E

N S J Y R Z E

N S J Y Z R E E R E

L M E L F B E

Q Z F H M A R   L M B R Z E

E V F Z Y - F Z H R Z

A F F G E

Q S E Y Z B   A V R T E

you can solve the rest, for if G stands for M in one word, it will be the same throughout the list. A new code is used for each Cryptoquiz.

Answers are on page 86.

3. CLOAK-AND-DAGGER FOLK

Example: intelligence officers

O E B S O

Q S R S Y R B G S O

L A Q S I Y X G S I

C U S A R O

Y X L A R S I O E B S O

Q X L P F S   C U S A R O

X E S I C R B G S O

B A G S O R B U C R X I O

O F S L R M O

"U L T O M X S O"

4. HAIRSTYLES

Example: bob

Z G N H Z J I

Z R L B F S F

"T S R M H D"

E L B I M L A V

E S F W I M L A V

U G M L C V

C J Z D I M L A

"P A M I I S E"

E S T E M C S J G

E M B N U S W

WORD CHARADE

To play Word Charade, find each letter in the diagram as defined in the instructions below. Then, write the letters down on the corresponding dashes. When you have found all of the letters, you will have spelled out a word with a "view."
Solution is on page 87.

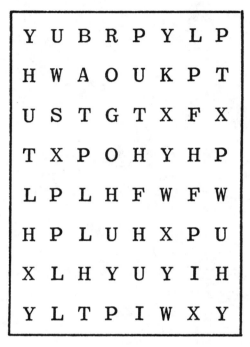

```
Y  U  B  R  P  Y  L  P
H  W  A  O  U  K  P  T
U  S  T  G  T  X  F  X
T  X  P  O  H  Y  H  P
L  P  L  H  F  W  F  W
H  P  L  U  H  X  P  U
X  L  H  Y  U  Y  I  H
Y  L  T  P  I  W  X  Y
```

$$\overline{}\ \overline{}\ \overline{}\ \overline{}\ \overline{}\ \overline{}\ \overline{}\ \overline{}$$

1   2   3   4   5   6   7   8

My 1st letter is above an X and below a W.

My 2nd letter is to the right of a U and to the left of a P.

My 3rd letter occurs 3 times in the same column.

My 4th letter is above an H which is above a T.

My 5th letter is below a P and has a Y on one side.

My 6th letter has the same vowel above and below it.

My 7th letter is to the left of an F and to the right of an L.

My 8th letter is between my 1st and 6th letter.

QUOTATION PUZZLES

To solve, fit the letters in each column of a puzzle into the boxes directly above them in order to form words. When you are through, you will discover a quotation by reading across the boxes in the diagram. The letters may or may not go into the boxes in the same order in which they are given; it is up to you to decide which letter goes into which box above it. Once a letter is used, cross it off the bottom half of the diagram and do not use it again. A black square indicates the end of a word.

The quotations are on page 87.

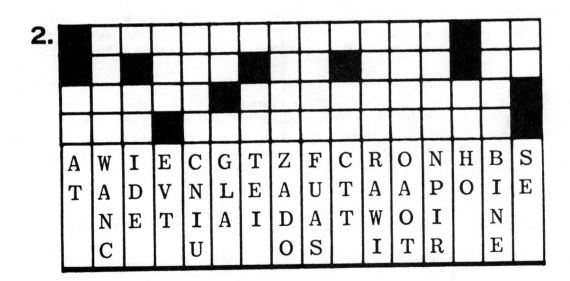

LETTER BANK

The object of LETTER BANK is to obtain the highest score possible by forming words on the dashes using only the letters given on the opposite page. To solve, proceed as follows:

1. Place the 12 letters given in the box on the opposite page into the numbered squares of the DIAGRAM in any order you wish. It's a good idea to try to place the letters that you think you will be using the most into the squares having the highest point value, since the number in each square will be used as the point value of the letter entered in that square. (You may find later on that you want to rearrange the positions of certain letters; that is allowed.)

2. Each word you form on the dashes MUST begin with the starting letters which are given. The number of dashes after these starting letters indicates the number of letters needed to complete that word; to be considered complete, each dash must have a letter on it. Use only the letters in the DIAGRAM to form your words; however, you need not use all the letters in the DIAGRAM, and you may use any letter as many times as you wish, even repeating it within a word. Try to form words composed of the highest value letters possible. Words beginning with a capital letter, slang, foreign, and poetic words are not allowed.

3. When you have completed all seven words, form the BONUS WORD by using only those letters that fall in the column indicated by the arrow. You may not be able to use all seven letters and you will probably have to rearrange them to form your word, but form the longest word you can. Do not use any letter more times than it appears in that column of letters.

4. To get your score, give each letter appearing over a dash in a completed word its point value (remember—a word cannot be considered complete if there is a dash without a letter over it). Add all these points together. Now add the point value of each letter in your BONUS WORD to the other points. This is your final score.

Average Score: 70   Good Score: 90   Excellent Score: 110 or more

Our solution, showing a score of 121 points, is on page 87.

$$\boxed{\text{B E G I L N O P R T V Y}}$$

DIAGRAM

2	3	4
2	3	4
2	3	4
2	3	4

Words   **Points**

↓

1. G L _ _ _ _   ___

2. A P _ _ _ _ _   ___

3. C A _ _ _ _   ___

4. F L _ _ _   ___

5. H A _ _ _ _   ___

6. K N _ _   ___

7. E M _ _ _ _   ___

Bonus Word

_ _ _ _ _ _ _   ___

CHANGELINGS

Can you change the first word into the second word (in each set below) by changing only one letter at a time? Do not rearrange the order of the letters. Each change must result in a real, everyday word; and words beginning with a capital letter, slang, contractions, or obsolete words are not allowed. The number in parentheses indicates the number of changes we used for that Changeling. Our answers are on page 87.

Example:

TINY to BIRD

(4 changes)

    TINY

1. TIN<u>s</u>

2. <u>b</u>INS

3. BIN<u>d</u>

4. BI<u>r</u>D

1. **S E E K to F I N D**   (4 changes)

2. **R O A D to J O I N**   (4 changes)

3. **F U E L to T A N K**   (5 changes)

4. **S I P S to M A L T**   (5 changes)

5. **L O N G to T A P E**   (5 changes)

NUMBER SQUARE

The magic number for this number square is 365. Fill in the empty boxes of the diagram in such a way that the following conditions are met: The five numbers in each row, each column, and each diagonal add up to 365. Some numbers may be used more than once. Some numbers have been entered to start you off.

Solution is on page 87.

77		61		75
83	65			
64		73	80	
70	72		81	68
	78	85		

LADDERGRAM

See directions on page 11.

Definitions

1. Responsibilities
2. Watches one's weight
3. Ocean current
4. Did the crawl or sidestroke
5. Used to be
6. While
7. Robins, wrens, etc.
8. Frees (of)
9. Physicians: abbr.
10. Wed
11. Navy's rival
12. Mr. Charles of music
13. Requires
14. Concludes
15. Cozy room
16. Mr. Morse or Clemens
17. Entertain
18. Identical
19. Traveled via ship
20. Thoughts
21. Fruit-juice drinks
22. Book of maps
23. Final
24. Misters Jolson and Pacino

1	2	3	
4	5	6	
7	8	9	
10	11	12	
13	14	15	
16	17	18	
19	20	21	
22	23	24	

Solution is on page 87

CRYPTOGRAMS

These Cryptograms are all in simple substitution codes—another letter of the alphabet is substituted for the right letter. THE WHITE DOG might be written RNS LNGRS MPI, R being used for T, N for H, S for E, etc. By noticing the frequency of certain letters (e, t, a, o, i, and n are usually the most frequently used letters in English) and by looking for patterns of letter repetition in the words, you should be able to "break" each code. Every Cryptogram is in a different code.

1. **Good news**   Z W T   X T Y P L E   Q W L

R Z Z Y R S Z P   A L L U   B L Y Z I E T

S R Y Y H T P   Q H Z W   W H N   Z W T

N R A E T Z   L B   X Y T X R Y R Z H L E .

2. **Happy thoughts**   R J W P   J A   T W   A Z M S   J M Q

S V X   J A   B J Y Y X   Z W   T W T V N N X

R J Y Q   P Y X Z M K   P C V M   V   B C J N Q

B Q Q L   J A   B J Y L .

3. **Mistakes really count**   X K C J Z   J E   Z X R

R K E J R E Z   Y K D   Z Q   C R   Y V Q W A

K A K J W .

4. **Be prepared!**   W S   N K H   O R Z H N R I ,   H N R

D N W E V ' A   A E R V   W A   S K H   O K I H N

" Z A D R S H . "

CRYPTOGRAMS

5. **Surprise me** BZT JPU AEHDG, QEN

FTNJQNMQ IHTQEGJU KDNJMYTN

AZRNM BTZR INHPF "FHBQ-

TJKQ."

6. **Just listen to us** WYACFA'H-CYAIFD

HLPM: XJK IMJZ JKA GJAM LH

DQF WAFHQFHD NFGYKHF DQF

FYAH HDLBB ZLPPBF.

7. **Calm down** WMTAK XDLZD AMKGEW

RAPI MIPWLPS TAM ZDMILZTEEJ

CLRRMAMSW RAPI WDPKM

ZTGKMC FJ LAALWTWLPS.

8. **A helpful hint** KMO QSVXZYW IZKT KTS

RVPXKN LR LKTSMN VN WSYKXO

VN IZKT OLPM LIY.

9. **Good memories** NBURBWH OPZU SOM

RSWZA ZBUHJBUMU NPO UJXXMO

ZSAZOMSXBWH.

Solutions are on page 87.

CROSS SUMS

In Cross Sums puzzles, the numbers in the black squares refer to the sum of the digits which you are to fill into the empty squares. The number ABOVE the diagonal line refers to the empty squares directly to the RIGHT of that number. A number BELOW the diagonal line refers to the empty squares directly BELOW that number.

No zeros are used here, only the digits one through nine. An important point: A digit cannot appear more than once in any particular digit combination. We have shaded one area in the diagram. If you need help starting the puzzle, the digit combination that goes into this shaded area is given on page 87.   Solution is on page 87.

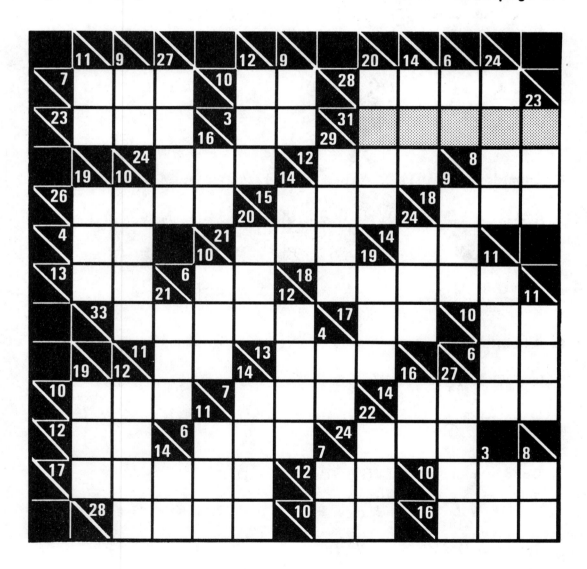

KRISS KROSS

Fit the words for each Kriss Kross into their proper places in the diagram, using as clues the length of the words, and the letters linking them to other words. The words are listed alphabetically according to the number of letters. Some Kriss Krosses have a word entered into the diagram to help you get started. In this puzzle, to proceed, find the 8-letter word or phrase beginning with the letter "P." Continue in this way until all the words are correctly placed.

3 LETTERS

Cat
Cow
Dog
Ewe
Kid
Pig
Ram
"Sit"
Vet
Zoo

4 LETTERS

Cage
Fish
Goat
Mutt
Pets
Pony
"Stay"

6 LETTERS

Cattle
Doctor

Horses
Kitten
Turtle

7 LETTERS

Animals
Examine
Healthy
"Nice cat!"
Puppies

8 LETTERS

Domestic

Hard work
Patients
"The sheep (are healthy)"

9 LETTERS

"Come in the (barn")
Creatures
Give a shot
Livestock
White mice

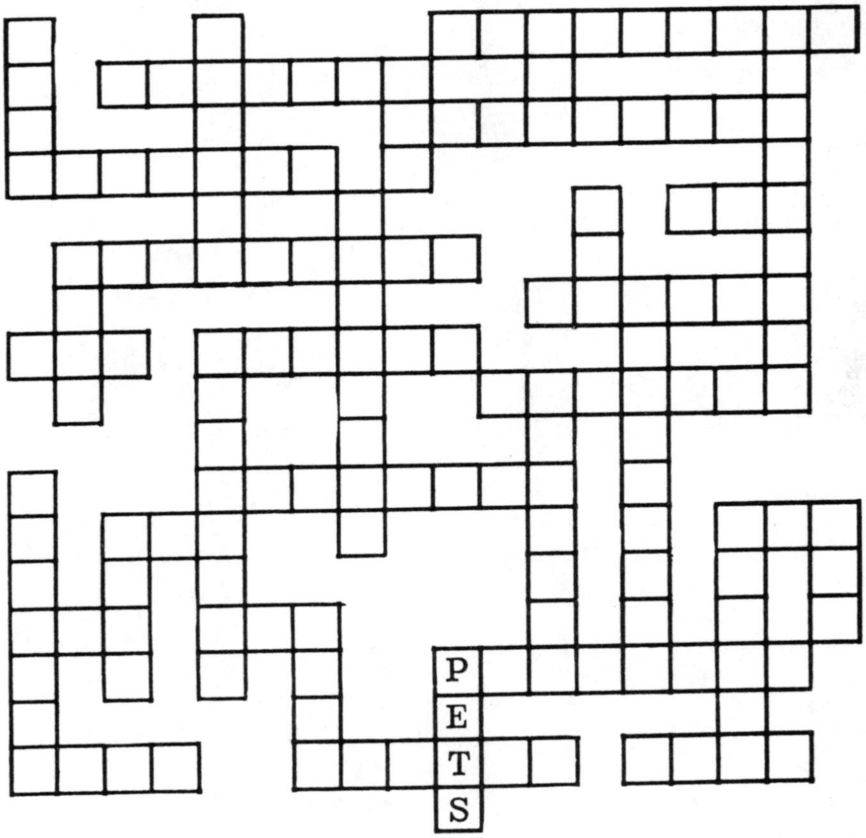

Solution is on page 88.

CRYPTOQUIZZES

A Cryptoquiz is a list of related words put into a simple code. Spot familiar words by their "patterns" of repeated or double letters, and

1. WATER WORDS
(All of these words follow the word WATER)

Example: wheel

B G A A

J R R A V T

X N P L Z

H M B B G A R

Y R A R

K R X V T

Y R X V T

Y N Z K R A

H V C

J F V Z K P M K

2. THEY ARE USED FOR CUTTING

Example: ax

Q D U

Q Z F Q Q N E Q

Y L F M J

Q K J D E Q

O N Z Y J R Y L F M J

E D B N E

Z I J D P J E

Z I F O O J E Q

K D Z Y Q D U

Q F Z Y I J

CRYPTOQUIZZES

you can solve the rest, for if G stands for M in one word, it will be the same throughout the list. A new code is used for each Cryptoquiz.

Answers are on page 88.

3. CITIES THAT BEGIN WITH "R"
Example: Roanoke (Va.)

D W A S

D C W   K S   O H V S C D W

D S V W

D W L N S P X S D

D C L N A W V K

D S H K C V Q

D W X X S D K H A

D H L C V S

D H V Q W W V

D H E S C Q N

4. THEY PREDICT THE FUTURE
Example: psychic

P M M Z

E J Z G K A M G M O O M Z

C P G Z J O J R M Z

P J J G U P C N M Z

X C O I   Z M C H M Z

E J Z M Y C P G M Z

J Z C Y O M

H L S L A M Z

Y O C L Z S J N C A G

X Z J R A J P G L Y C G J Z

NUMBER SQUARE

One of the numbers one through eight is to be filled into each of the white squares in the diagram below. You may use the same number more than once in doing so. Can you deduce from the clues what number should go into each of the squares? The second digit in 6-Across is entered to start you off. Note that, while each answer to the clues will be a three or four-digit number, only one digit is to go into each square.

ACROSS

1. A perfect square which is larger than 100 and smaller than 196 (example: 121 is a perfect square, since $11 \times 11 = 121$)

4. The number formed by the first two digits is divisible by 9, and so is the number formed by the last two digits

6. The missing digits include 5 and 7

7. The sum of the three digits is 19

DOWN

1. The second digit is twice the first; the third is twice the second

2. Four consecutive digits, not necessarily in order

3. Four consecutive digits, not necessarily in order

5. Three consecutive digits in ascending order

1	2	3	■
4			5
6	6		
■	7		

Solution is on page 88.

58

RING AROUND THE SQUARE

Enter the words that fit the definitions into the diagram in a clockwise direction, beginning with A-1. In each of the rings of squares—A, B, C, and D—each word overlaps the next one by one or more letters, and the last word in each ring overlaps the first word in that ring. (For example, A-7 overlaps A-1.) When the puzzle is completed, the circled letters, reading from upper left to lower right, will spell out a word related to the theme of the puzzle.

A-1. Female restaurant employee
A-2. Group of employees
A-3. James Galway or the Pied Piper
A-4. Employee in the secretarial pool
A-5. Farmer's vehicle
A-6. "Home on the —"
A-7. — grease, physical effort

B-1. Place of business
B-2. Delivery person made obsolete by the refrigerator
B-3. Florence Nightingale, for one
B-4. High-ranking lawmakers
B-5. — and bonds
B-6. Work space for an artist or photographer

C-1. Mechanical laborer
C-2. Private teacher
C-3. Disc-jockey's medium
C-4. Refinery product
C-5. Tanner's product

D-1. Oven for a potter
D-2. Fisherman's equipment
D-3. Lion —, circus performer
D-4. Skater's arena

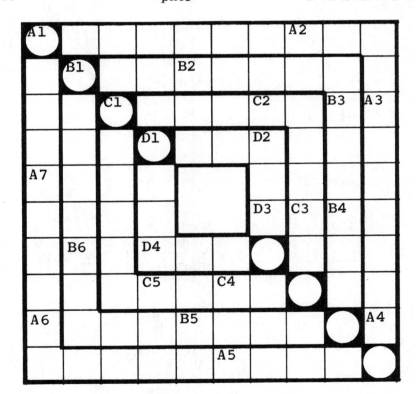

Solution is on page 88.

CRYPTOGRAMS

These Cryptograms are all in simple substitution codes—another letter of the alphabet is substituted for the right letter. **THE WHITE DOG** might be written RNS LNGRS MPI, R being used for T, N for H, S for E, etc. By noticing the frequency of certain letters (e, t, a, o, i, and n are usually the most frequently used letters in English) and by looking for patterns of letter repetition in the words, you should be able to "break" each code. Every Cryptogram is in a different code.

1. **Lost and found**   V N X   T B U   I N C   M C K X

   N W K   N X B E   W K   V N X   M B K V   C U X

   V C   T W K K   W V .

2. **Growing gains**   M L D   Z H S D V   Y   W V Z X ,

   M L D   U Z V D   Y   S Y Q M V T Q M   M L D

   B Z U U Z R   Y S D K   M L K M   K W D

   N V Y R W Q   T Q   X Y Q S Z U .

3. **The mirror doesn't lie**   I V Q G Z N   T Y B ' Z

   V M V F N Z J T B U ,   I G Z   T Z   T Y   Q

   M V F N   U L L S   Z J T B U   Z L   Y V V .

4. **Family trees**   O T M T P V H X   D Q K Z T Z   Q

   B T M Z L W ' Z   B Q M T W H Z   H L   C L W P T M

   Q   U V H   Q U L K H   T Q D O   L H O T M .

5. **Good advice** SW CBSCB FHQMBIZSP

FLBSFJ GZIBC FW PW DZCYZSP

LYBS JWT AQS VB QC

TSCTAABCCDTI SBQH YWGB.

6. **Stay warm** EWFL SYRLHME TJH KL

YLJB TWFSWYZLYE, UNRBL

WZNLYE JYL ULZ KBJHQLZE.

7. **Hold on** FUMZ JU FVVFIWTUSWP

BJH VJHHZR QP, SW MJUUFW QZ

IZMJVWTIZR.

8. **A good formula** YJQ KTPG WL JDKRF

GTFMFQOO XTPP NQRY BWPM

BVQRK LWV XVTFGPQO.

9. **Help!** POCY C YCJKFLA PLZ PL ICJ

PLCEL POLJ PL ZLKMJ FLCSJMJK

YU ISUIOLY.

Solutions are on page 88.

CRYPTOGRAMS

(Starting helps for these Cryptograms are on page 88.)

10. New rules G N W D   F I   R C A T I   T C O Q I
N R I D H   M D T D A W D T   F   T D E N H M
O G F H E D .

11. Drive carefully F L C Q   M P V Z H   J Z X Y
Z X K V K B P G Z   D L C Z Q L V   F J K X Z   L B
X L B M   G C K Y H .

12. Neatness counts J Q G W M B   Y F M G W   Q J Z
Q F C   D P X K   K W F M X - J P H C W Z
P H P X P F J B .

13. A green thumb B Y V V Y F G M H B   P M Z
V P V H X   V W G P H G   V K F K W Q Y F
Z G B G W H   K P B X B .

14. Relax! C B P H L H Q F   V H J Y   R T W Y X V
J W V Q   T J H R H Q W B T C   R X V H Q F
B W C L .

CHALLENGER

15. Safety first K D N   G X R P W Q D Z L   K Q X R P W
T X S C H F D C   G X F Z ,   D W X Q F H L W
M X M S Q F G   R F T M N G X S C Z .

Solutions are on page 88.

KRISS KROSS

It took our best Kriss Krosser 23 minutes to complete this puzzle, with the same head start you have—LEMON entered in its correct place in the diagram. See how long it takes you to solve it, if you like to work against time. Your solving time:

3 LETTERS	Foal	Amore	Memel
Ami	Into	Comma	Minim
Dem	Lime	Denim	Modem
Eon	Loan	Dogma	Naomi
Man	Mama	Doing	Negro
Mao	Mono	Dunno	Nobel
Moi	Omen	Ennui	No one
Off	Omoo	Enorm	Ollie
One	Unum	Folio	Oomph
Ono	Whom	Impel	Orion
4 LETTERS	Zoom	Ionic	Orono
Ally	**5 LETTERS**	Lemon	Ozone
Boll	Allen	Magna	Rollo
Emma	Alloy	Mamie	Women

Solution is on page 88.

LETTER CHASE

Solve Letter Chase as follows:

1. Choose letters from the Letter List to complete the words started on the page opposite. Always proceed from left to right in choosing letters, and cross off letters as you use them. Do not double back in the Letter List once you've begun to select letters for a word, and do not rearrange their order in any way once you've selected them. Letters must be selected in the same order as you use them in the word, but they do not have to appear together in the Letter List. The crossed-off letters may not be used again.

2. Formed words must be at least three letters long, but do not form any word by adding more letters than there are blank dashes.

In this puzzle, for example: L E __ __ __ could be **LET**, **LEG**, **LEAN** or **LEAVE** (among others).

3. Form only common English words. Words beginning with a capital letter, obsolete or foreign words, and plurals are not allowed.

SCORING: Give yourself 5 points for each word formed, plus 1 point for every one of the letters in the formed word, including the letters given. Subtract 10 points from your total score for every word that can't be formed. A score of 70 points is passable; 80 points is average; 90 points is good; 100 points is perfect. To get a perfect score, all the letters must be used.

Our answer, which may not agree with yours, is on page 89.

LETTER LIST

O T A C E V G A M T O L E A I W O N R X H C T K L R I N E D A L Y

Words   **Points**

1. S L __ __   ____

2. M __ __ __ __   ____

3. L E __ __ __   ____

4. A N __ __ __ __   ____

5. H __ __ __   ____

6. G L __ __ __   ____

7. R __ __ __ __ __   ____

8. W A __ __ __   ____

9. B O __ __   ____

10. V A __ __ __   ____

KRISS KROSS

It took our best Kriss Krosser 20 minutes to complete this puzzle, with the same head start you have—SMART entered in its correct place in the diagram. See how long it takes you to solve it, if you like to work against time. Your solving time:

5 LETTERS

Abaca

Armor

Aroma

Cameo

Canal

Coati

Cusec

Emote

Erase

Error

Ester

Ewing

Hanoi

Hello

Incan

Lanai

Matte

Moist

Naomi

Ocala

Olein

Osmic

Outer

Reach

Relic

Reset

Rumor

Sinai

Since

Sitar

Smart

Strum

Tarot

Tears

Touch

Uncle

Wheel

Solution is on page 89

66

LOGIC PROBLEM

THE FIVE STATE BAND   by Lois K. Bohnsack

This year the winner of the WLCMF (We Love Country Music Fans) Top Group Award was the Five State Band. Each member of the band plays a different musical instrument. The group is based in Tennessee; however, only one member is a native of that State. From the clues below, can you determine each member's full name, his home State, and the instrument he plays? The first name of one is Bob; the surname of one is Knight.

1. Carl, who is not Mr. Granger, plays the guitar.
2. Neither the piano player nor Adam is from Alabama or Kentucky.
3. The five members are: Earl, Mr. Jackson, Mr. Granger, the piano player, and the man from Texas.
4. The banjo player is not from Alabama.
5. Neither Mr. Jackson nor Mr. Ingram is from North Carolina.
6. Three of the men are Adam, Mr. Granger, and the fiddle player (who is not Mr. Ingram).
7. Mr. Harris and the man from Alabama met at music school.
8. The man from Texas does not play the drums or banjo.
9. Dennis is not Mr. Granger or Mr. Harris.

Solution is on page 89.

Use the chart below to help sort the information given in the clues. Use an X to indicate "no" for an eliminated possibility and a dot to indicate "yes" for a confirmed conclusion. Once you enter a definite "yes" (dot), put an X for "no" in the rest of the boxes in each row and column that contains the dot.

	Gra.	Har.	Ing.	Jac.	Kni.	Ala.	Ky.	N.C.	Tenn.	Tex.	ba.	dr.	fi.	gu.	pi.
Adam															
Bob															
Carl															
Den.															
Earl															
ba.															
dr.															
fi.															
gu.															
pi.															
Ala.															
Ky.															
N.C.															
Tenn.															
Tex.															

LADDERGRAM

by IRENE R. HAYES

First write the word that fits definition 1 into space 1. Then drop one letter and rearrange the remaining letters to form the answer to definition 2. Drop one more letter, rearrange, and get the answer to definition 3. Put the first dropped letter into the box to the left of space 1 and the other dropped letter into the box to the right of space 3. When you've correctly solved the puzzle, the dropped letters in the boxes on the left and those on the right, when read down, will spell out related words.   Solution is on page 89.

Definitions

1. Drills (a hole) into

2. Ascended

3. Metal source

4. "Do unto — . . ."

5. Brief, as a speech

6. Decays

7. Birchbark boat

8. Starting word in a fairy tale

9. 100 years: abbr.

10. Cost

11. Ready for harvesting

12. Crusted dessert

13. Trustworthy

14. Small rock

15. Coal weights

1	2	3	
4	5	6	
7	8	9	
10	11	12	
13	14	15	

KRISS KROSS

This Kriss Kross is not that tough, but it makes a good warm-up for the Kriss Krosses on the following pages. All starting and final L's have been entered in the diagram as a help.

3 LETTERS
Lac (*resinous substance*)
Lea
Lei
Lek (*Albanian monetary unit*)

4 LETTERS
Lena
Lieu
Lion
Loan
Loll
Love

5 LETTERS
Label
Lease
Least
Liana
Llama
Lloyd
Local
Lodge
Lucky

6 LETTERS
Labile (*unstable*)
Lambda (*Greek letter*)

Lassie
League
Leeway
Lentic (*in still water*)
Lentil
Lesson
Lierne (*Architectural feature*)
Lillie
Locate
Logger
Loiter

7 LETTERS
Lanolin

Learned
Leucite
Levulin (*carbohydrate*)
Lidless
Lucania (*Ancient district in Italy*)
Lycopod

8 LETTERS
Lazulite
Legation
Lenitive
Licorice
Low-grade

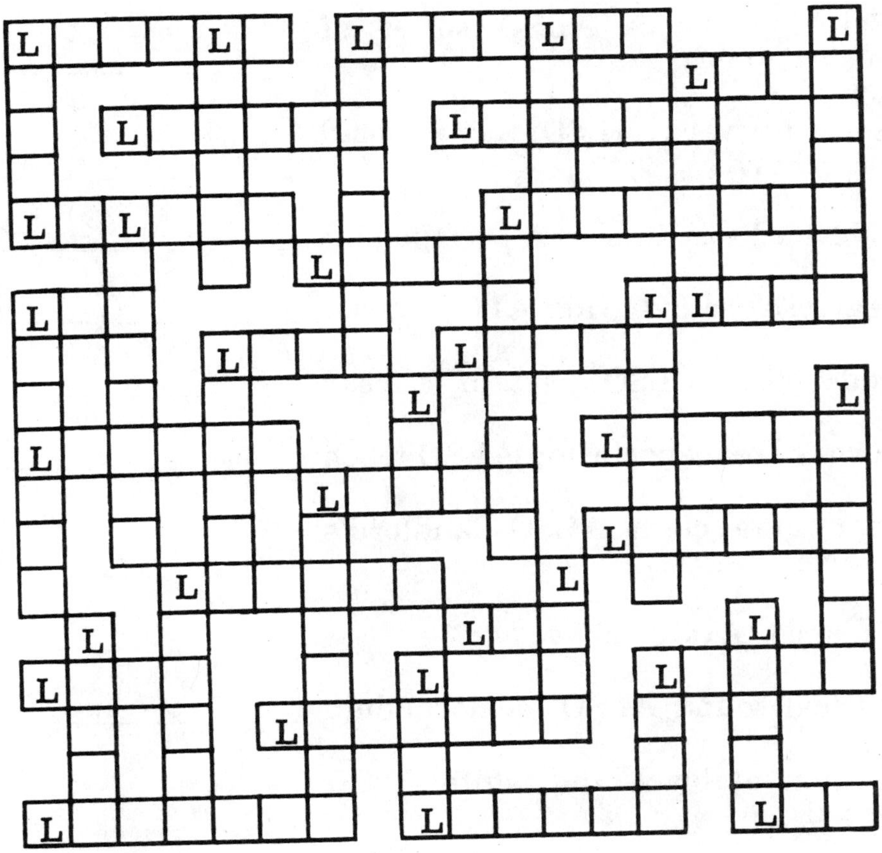

Solution is on page 89

DOUBLE-NITIONS

Many of our everyday words have more than one meaning. Below, at left, are fourteen pairs of definitions; both definitions in each pair fit the same word, which should be entered on the space provided on the right. When read down, the first letters of the fourteen answer words will spell out the name of a famous American. Answers are on page 89.

1. Parking area ALSO considerable quantity _____

2. Not divisible by two ALSO unusual _____

3. Absolute; total ALSO pronounce _____

4. Large, showy flower ALSO part of the eye _____

5. Weighing device ALSO series of musical tones _____

6. Move forward ALSO money paid beforehand _____

7. Give back an image ALSO ponder _____

8. Coarsely ground grain ALSO repast _____

9. Add spices ALSO part of a year _____

10. Form of transportation ALSO teach _____

11. Tear in a cloth ALSO landlord's income _____

12. Finished ALSO above _____

13. Musical sound ALSO memorandum _____

14. Mixture of black and white ALSO dismal _____

WORD ARITHMETIC

These are simply long-division problems in which letters are substituted for the numbers 0 to 9. Solve each problem, writing every letter, as you discover its value, above the correct number on the line provided. When you are finished, the letters will spell out a word or phrase.

Answers are on page 89.

1. ‾0‾1‾2‾3‾4‾5‾6‾7‾8‾9‾

```
                    S I L K
          SKI ) C L A S S I C
                A I C S
                C H B S
                C T A H
                  I M I
                  S K I
                  A A B C
                  A L T T
                    L S
```

2. ‾0‾1‾2‾3‾4‾5‾6‾7‾8‾9‾

```
                      B R A N
        GNAT ) E A R R I N G
               G N A T
               B R B I I
               B B M B N
                 G B G N G
                 D M D E R
                   G B B I
```

3. ‾0‾1‾2‾3‾4‾5‾6‾7‾8‾9‾

```
                      E L K
        YOKE ) L E G A L L Y
               L I A F O
               O A L F L
               O F A G I
                 F T O K Y
                 F A G O Y
                   L O A G
```

4. ‾0‾1‾2‾3‾4‾5‾6‾7‾8‾9‾

```
                        P I E
        HEEL ) G R A P H I C
               I E E C R
               A A H I
               H E E L
               H A H P C
               H P E L T
                 I H E T
```

KRISS KROSS

Fit the words for each Kriss Kross into their proper places in the diagram, using as clues the length of the words, and the letters linking them to other words. The words are listed alphabetically according to the number of letters. Some Kriss Krosses have a word entered into the diagram to help you get started. In this puzzle, to proceed, find the 8-letter word with "S" as its first letter. Continue in this way until all the words are correctly placed.

3 LETTERS
Add
Due
Pay
Sum

4 LETTERS
Bank
Bond
Coin (*wrappers*)
Dime
Half (*dollar*)
Lend

Mint
Rate (*of interest*)

5 LETTERS
Board (*of directors*)
Cents
Funds
Money
Paper (*money*)
Total

6 LETTERS
Amount
Branch (*offices*)
Credit
Fiscal

7 LETTERS
Balance
"Banker's (*hours*")
Deposit
Quarter

8 LETTERS
Monetary
Mortgage
Receipts
Subtract
Treasury (*notes*)

10 LETTERS
Cash a check
Circulated (*currency*)
Grant a loan
In the vault

Solution is on page 90

L A D D E R G R A M

by **IRENE R. HAYES**

First write the word that fits definition 1 into space 1. Then drop one letter and rearrange the remaining letters to form the answer to definition 2. Drop one more letter, rearrange, and get the answer to definition 3. Put the first dropped letter into the box to the left of space 1 and the other dropped letter into the box to the right of space 3. When you've correctly solved the puzzle, the dropped letters in the boxes on the left and those on the right, when read down, will spell out related words.

Solution is on page 90.

Definitions

1. Tire mishaps

2. Final

3. Messrs. Pacino and Jolson

4. TV collie

5. Store events

6. Girl; miss

7. — the score, ties the game

8. Victory letters or signs

9. Adam's mate

10. No longer fresh, as bread

11. Allows

12. Overhead railways

13. Learn one's —, learn by experience

14. "Schnozzes"

15. Dollar bills

1	2	3	
4	5	6	
7	8	9	
10	11	12	
13	14	15	

FIGGERITS

1. Answer all the Definitions you can. 2. Transfer the letters of the Words to the Solution blanks below according to matching numbers. 3. Work back and forth from Solution to Words for added help. The Solution, when filled in, will be a little truism. Letters (and numbers) may be repeated in the Words column. Solutions are on page 90; word lists are on page 90.

1

Definitions   Words

Disappear .... $\overline{12}$ $\overline{11}$ $\overline{4}$ $\overline{17}$ $\overline{21}$ $\overline{44}$

Pause indecisively .... $\overline{25}$ $\overline{7}$ $\overline{21}$ $\overline{17}$ $\overline{43}$ $\overline{26}$ $\overline{16}$ $\overline{30}$

Opinion .... $\overline{12}$ $\overline{17}$ $\overline{8}$ $\overline{37}$ $\overline{31}$ $\overline{47}$ $\overline{17}$ $\overline{4}$ $\overline{28}$

Joe —, 49er's quarterback .... $\overline{22}$ $\overline{3}$ $\overline{19}$ $\overline{28}$ $\overline{45}$ $\overline{36}$ $\overline{13}$

Brainless one in "The Wizard ...... of Oz" $\overline{42}$ $\overline{24}$ $\overline{15}$ $\overline{33}$ $\overline{8}$ $\overline{14}$ $\overline{33}$ $\overline{2}$ $\overline{37}$

Mouth organ .... $\overline{38}$ $\overline{13}$ $\overline{33}$ $\overline{22}$ $\overline{47}$ $\overline{1}$ $\overline{17}$ $\overline{24}$ $\overline{20}$

Jacques —, captain of the .... "Calypso" $\overline{14}$ $\overline{35}$ $\overline{23}$ $\overline{10}$ $\overline{28}$ $\overline{49}$ $\overline{11}$ $\overline{41}$

Capital of Iowa: 2 wds. .... $\overline{9}$ $\overline{30}$ $\overline{34}$ $\overline{22}$ $\overline{39}$ $\overline{17}$ $\overline{48}$ $\overline{5}$ $\overline{27}$

"Meet —," 1941 Gary Cooper ...... film: 2 wds. $\overline{40}$ $\overline{3}$ $\overline{29}$ $\overline{6}$ $\overline{46}$ $\overline{18}$ $\overline{32}$

Solution: $\overline{}$ $\frac{}{1}$ $\frac{}{2}$ $\frac{}{3}$ $\frac{}{4}$ $\frac{}{5}$ $\frac{}{6}$ $\frac{}{7}$ $\frac{}{8}$ $\frac{}{9}$ $\frac{}{10}$ $\frac{}{11}$

$\frac{}{12}$ $\frac{}{13}$ $\frac{}{14}$ $\frac{}{15}$ $\frac{}{16}$ $\frac{}{17}$ $\frac{}{18}$ $\frac{}{19}$ $\frac{}{20}$ $\frac{}{21}$ $\frac{}{22}$ $\frac{}{23}$ $\frac{}{24}$ $\frac{}{25}$ $\frac{}{26}$ $\frac{}{27}$

$\frac{}{28}$ $\frac{}{29}$ $\frac{}{30}$ $\frac{}{31}$ $\frac{}{32}$ $\frac{}{33}$ $\frac{}{34}$ $\frac{}{35}$ $\frac{}{36}$ $\frac{}{37}$ $\frac{}{38}$ $\frac{}{39}$ $\frac{}{40}$ $\frac{}{41}$ $\frac{}{42}$ $\frac{}{43}$

$\frac{}{44}$ $\frac{}{45}$ $\frac{}{46}$ $\frac{}{47}$ $\frac{}{48}$ $\frac{}{49}$

FIGGERITS

Definitions   Words

Mr. Bell's invention .... $\overline{11}$ $\overline{29}$ $\overline{18}$ $\overline{26}$ $\overline{7}$ $\overline{13}$ $\overline{19}$ $\overline{3}$ $\overline{16}$

Coleslaw, for one .... $\overline{5}$ $\overline{24}$ $\overline{8}$ $\overline{2}$ $\overline{27}$

Knight's garb .... $\overline{9}$ $\overline{28}$ $\overline{1}$ $\overline{14}$ $\overline{22}$

Masculine title .... $\overline{31}$ $\overline{4}$ $\overline{23}$ $\overline{11}$ $\overline{21}$ $\overline{25}$

Highway divisions .... $\overline{18}$ $\overline{30}$ $\overline{3}$ $\overline{21}$ $\overline{15}$

Less dangerous .... $\overline{32}$ $\overline{6}$ $\overline{17}$ $\overline{16}$ $\overline{22}$

A house's "eyes" .... $\overline{20}$ $\overline{4}$ $\overline{10}$ $\overline{27}$ $\overline{19}$ $\overline{12}$ $\overline{15}$

Solution: $\overline{1}$ $\overline{2}$ $\overline{3}$ $\overline{4}$ $\overline{5}$ $\overline{6}$ $\overline{7}$ $\overline{8}$ $\overline{9}$ $\overline{10}$ $\overline{11}$

$\overline{12}$ $\overline{13}$ $\overline{14}$ $\overline{15}$ $\overline{16}$ $\overline{17}$ $\overline{18}$ $\overline{19}$ $\overline{20}$ $\overline{21}$ $\overline{22}$ $\overline{23}$ $\overline{24}$ $\overline{25}$ $\overline{26}$

$\overline{27}$ $\overline{28}$ $\overline{29}$ $\overline{30}$ $\overline{31}$ $\overline{32}$

Fido's "pal" .... $\overline{15}$ $\overline{11}$ $\overline{8}$ $\overline{26}$ $\overline{27}$

People on the distaff side .... $\overline{25}$ $\overline{11}$ $\overline{10}$ $\overline{28}$ $\overline{18}$

Make ice cubes .... $\overline{14}$ $\overline{12}$ $\overline{9}$ $\overline{17}$ $\overline{32}$ $\overline{2}$

Flower found in a moor .... $\overline{22}$ $\overline{13}$ $\overline{29}$ $\overline{21}$ $\overline{6}$ $\overline{2}$ $\overline{27}$

Ultimate .... $\overline{14}$ $\overline{16}$ $\overline{24}$ $\overline{3}$ $\overline{30}$

Aunts and uncles .... $\overline{27}$ $\overline{17}$ $\overline{4}$ $\overline{23}$ $\overline{21}$ $\overline{31}$ $\overline{8}$ $\overline{26}$ $\overline{20}$

Permitted .... $\overline{7}$ $\overline{30}$ $\overline{5}$ $\overline{11}$ $\overline{1}$ $\overline{33}$ $\overline{19}$

Solution: $\overline{1}$ $\overline{2}$ $\overline{3}$ $\overline{4}$ $\overline{5}$ $\overline{6}$ $\overline{7}$ $\overline{8}$ $\overline{9}$ $\overline{10}$ $\overline{11}$ $\overline{12}$ $\overline{13}$

$\overline{14}$ $\overline{15}$ $\overline{16}$ $\overline{17}$ $\overline{18}$ $\overline{19}$ $\overline{20}$ $\overline{21}$ $\overline{22}$ $\overline{23}$ $\overline{24}$ $\overline{25}$ $\overline{26}$

$\overline{27}$ $\overline{28}$ $\overline{29}$ $\overline{30}$ $\overline{31}$ $\overline{32}$ $\overline{33}$

FIGGERITS

4

Definitions   Words

Comedian on the "Road to Rio": .... ___ ___ ___ ___ ___ ___ ___
2 wds.   12   17   29   9   2   15   35

"— Georgia Brown" .... ___ ___ ___ ___ ___
                              21   11   30   32   28

Hero of Sherwood Forest: .... ___ ___ ___ ___ ___ ___ ___ ___ ___
2 wds.   33   10   29   25   1   9   17   2   14

Gentlemen's —, unwritten .... ___ ___ ___ ___ ___ ___ ___ ___ ___
understanding   4   26   16   35   32   3   30   1   6

Writer Woolf .... ___ ___ ___ ___ ___ ___ ___ ___
                              31   22   8   26   20   1   25   13

Stutter .... ___ ___ ___ ___ ___ ___ ___
                              18   23   13   3   24   7   33

Not more than: 3 wds. .... ___ ___ ___ ___ ___ ___ ___ ___ ___
                              13   5   23   27   19   24   2   34   6

Solution: ___ ___   ___ ___ ___ ___ ___ ___   ___ ___ ___
          1   2   3   4   5   6   7   8   9   10   11

___ ___ ___   ___ ___ ___ ___ ___   ___ ___   ___ ___
12   13   14   15   16   17   18   19   20   21   22   23

___ ___ ___ ___ ___   ___ ___   ___ ___ ___ ___ ___
24   25   26   27   28   29   30   31   32   33   34   35

5

Selection .... ___ ___ ___ ___ ___ ___
                            16   5   34   25   4   9

Goes (to school) .... ___ ___ ___ ___ ___ ___ ___
                            31   33   30   11   24   8   14

Court exhibit .... ___ ___ ___ ___ ___ ___ ___ ___
                            18   10   6   8   11   32   17   36

Coloring book companions .... ___ ___ ___ ___ ___ ___ ___
                            4   29   3   13   28   35   20

Progenitor .... ___ ___ ___ ___ ___ ___
                            27   31   12   18   35   1

Classroom subject .... ___ ___ ___ ___ ___ ___ ___
                            5   21   19   33   2   29   13

"Evita" or "Oklahoma" .... ___ ___ ___ ___ ___ ___ ___
                            26   15   22   21   16   23   7

Solution: ___ ___   ___   ___ ___ ___ ___ ___   ___ ___ ___ ___ ___
          1   2   3   4   5   6   7   8   9   10   11   12   13

___ ___ ___ ___ ___ ___ ___   ___ ___   ___ ___
14   15   16   17   18   19   20   21   22   23   24

___ ___ ___ ___ ___ ___ ___ ___ ___   ___ ___ ___
25   26   27   28   29   30   31   32   33   34   35   36

FIGGERITS

Slant .... $\overline{7}$ $\overline{35}$ $\overline{12}$ $\overline{31}$ $\overline{14}$ $\overline{24}$ $\overline{32}$

Highest point .... $\overline{19}$ $\overline{4}$ $\overline{24}$ $\overline{1}$ $\overline{29}$ $\overline{22}$

Undiplomatic .... $\overline{15}$ $\overline{5}$ $\overline{17}$ $\overline{25}$ $\overline{31}$ $\overline{20}$ $\overline{6}$ $\overline{3}$

Some siblings .... $\overline{27}$ $\overline{33}$ $\overline{30}$ $\overline{10}$ $\overline{22}$ $\overline{20}$ $\overline{13}$ $\overline{6}$

Of the East .... $\overline{26}$ $\overline{33}$ $\overline{16}$ $\overline{8}$ $\overline{24}$ $\overline{2}$ $\overline{23}$ $\overline{31}$

Garret .... $\overline{34}$ $\overline{25}$ $\overline{36}$ $\overline{18}$ $\overline{17}$

Original invention .... $\overline{12}$ $\overline{9}$ $\overline{28}$ $\overline{34}$ $\overline{21}$ $\overline{18}$ $\overline{11}$ $\overline{35}$

Solution: $\overline{1}$ $\overline{2}$ $\overline{3}$ $\overline{4}$ $\overline{5}$ $\overline{6}$ $\overline{7}$ $\overline{8}$ $\overline{9}$ $\overline{10}$ $\overline{11}$

$\overline{12}$ $\overline{13}$ $\overline{14}$ $\overline{15}$ $\overline{16}$ $\overline{17}$ $\overline{18}$ $\overline{19}$ $\overline{20}$ $\overline{21}$ $\overline{22}$ $\overline{23}$ $\overline{24}$ $\overline{25}$ $\overline{26}$

$\overline{27}$ $\overline{28}$ $\overline{29}$ $\overline{30}$ $\overline{31}$ $\overline{32}$ $\overline{33}$ $\overline{34}$ $\overline{35}$ $\overline{36}$

Difficulty .... $\overline{32}$ $\overline{7}$ $\overline{28}$ $\overline{21}$ $\overline{10}$ $\overline{1}$ $\overline{15}$ $\overline{24}$

Et cetera: 3 wds. .... $\overline{7}$ $\overline{16}$ $\overline{21}$ $\overline{10}$ $\overline{23}$ $\overline{12}$ $\overline{34}$

Baby .... $\overline{33}$ $\overline{11}$ $\overline{26}$ $\overline{7}$ $\overline{29}$ $\overline{13}$

Florence —, of "The Brady Bunch" . $\overline{1}$ $\overline{20}$ $\overline{16}$ $\overline{21}$ $\overline{9}$ $\overline{28}$ $\overline{10}$ $\overline{30}$ $\overline{18}$

Flying: 3 wds. .... $\overline{27}$ $\overline{34}$ $\overline{13}$ $\overline{22}$ $\overline{19}$ $\overline{3}$ $\overline{33}$ $\overline{18}$ $\overline{35}$

One of the 13 original States ...... $\overline{17}$ $\overline{20}$ $\overline{5}$ $\overline{8}$ $\overline{35}$ $\overline{15}$ $\overline{7}$

Quick-tempered; rash .... $\overline{4}$ $\overline{27}$ $\overline{31}$ $\overline{14}$ $\overline{25}$ $\overline{7}$ $\overline{21}$ $\overline{2}$ $\overline{6}$

Solution: $\overline{1}$ $\overline{2}$ $\overline{3}$ $\overline{4}$ $\overline{5}$ $\overline{6}$ $\overline{7}$ $\overline{8}$ $\overline{9}$ $\overline{10}$

$\overline{11}$ $\overline{12}$ $\overline{13}$ $\overline{14}$ $\overline{15}$ $\overline{16}$ $\overline{17}$ $\overline{18}$ $\overline{19}$ $\overline{20}$ $\overline{21}$ $\overline{22}$ $\overline{23}$ $\overline{24}$ $\overline{25}$

$\overline{26}$ $\overline{27}$ $\overline{28}$ $\overline{29}$ $\overline{30}$ $\overline{31}$ $\overline{32}$ $\overline{33}$ $\overline{34}$ $\overline{35}$

Solutions are on page 90; word lists are on page 90.

FIGGERITS

8

Definitions	Words

Eat .... ‾7‾ ‾26‾ ‾16‾ ‾25‾ ‾32‾ ‾2‾ ‾19‾

Sudden rushes of wind .... ‾21‾ ‾32‾ ‾25‾ ‾13‾ ‾1‾

Enrage .... ‾3‾ ‾16‾ ‾33‾ ‾28‾ ‾11‾ ‾9‾ ‾24‾

High and —, arrogant .... ‾31‾ ‾15‾ ‾21‾ ‾14‾ ‾20‾ ‾30‾

Dance wear .... ‾10‾ ‾22‾ ‾17‾ ‾34‾ ‾20‾ ‾6‾

Rotate .... ‾29‾ ‾19‾ ‾23‾ ‾12‾ ‾4‾ ‾27‾ ‾5‾

Soon .... ‾9‾ ‾14‾ ‾8‾ ‾29‾ ‾10‾ ‾4‾ ‾18‾

Solution: ‾1‾ ‾2‾ ‾3‾ ‾4‾ ‾5‾ ‾6‾ ‾7‾ ‾8‾ ‾9‾ ‾10‾

‾11‾ ‾12‾ ‾13‾ ‾14‾ ‾15‾ ‾16‾ ‾17‾ ‾18‾ ‾19‾ ‾20‾ ‾21‾ ‾22‾ ‾23‾ ‾24‾ ‾25‾ ‾26‾

‾27‾ ‾28‾ ‾29‾ ‾30‾ ‾31‾ ‾32‾ ‾33‾ ‾34‾

9

Deaden sound by covering .... ‾32‾ ‾12‾ ‾16‾ ‾23‾ ‾14‾ ‾30‾

Healthful .... ‾3‾ ‾17‾ ‾15‾ ‾13‾ ‾31‾ ‾7‾ ‾9‾ ‾19‾ ‾2‾

Flexible; supple .... ‾14‾ ‾24‾ ‾34‾ ‾1‾ ‾21‾

Annoying summer pest .... ‾32‾ ‾10‾ ‾20‾ ‾26‾ ‾12‾ ‾24‾ ‾8‾ ‾5‾

Kind of "visit" or "letter": .... ‾16‾ ‾10‾ ‾13‾ ‾22‾ ‾15‾ ‾3‾ ‾27‾ ‾33‾
   hyph. wd.

Guided rocket .... ‾19‾ ‾28‾ ‾20‾ ‾25‾ ‾6‾ ‾13‾ ‾2‾

Deceitful .... ‾25‾ ‾4‾ ‾18‾ ‾11‾ ‾29‾ ‾35‾

Solution: ‾1‾ ‾2‾ ‾3‾ ‾4‾ ‾5‾ ‾6‾ ‾7‾ ‾8‾ ‾9‾ ‾10‾

‾11‾ ‾12‾ ‾13‾ ‾14‾ ‾15‾ ‾16‾ ‾17‾ ‾18‾ ‾19‾ ‾20‾ ‾21‾ ‾22‾ ‾23‾ ‾24‾ ‾25‾

‾26‾ ‾27‾ ‾28‾ ‾29‾ ‾30‾ ‾31‾ ‾32‾ ‾33‾ ‾34‾ ‾35‾

Solutions are on page 90; word lists are on page 90.

Answers

KRISS KROSS — Page 1

```
S T P A U L S       A
H     N     O   P R I N C E S S D I
R     N     N   C         A       A
O N E   D U C H E S S     R     W
N           N   B         T I A R A
W E D D I N G   I         L     H   L   S
I           A   S         E     R   E   T
L A U R A       H             C R O W N   S H Y
L       A   C R O W N         U     T   L
I     F I V E             A   C H A R L E S H
A     N     N         A   W       T   Y   L
M     E     G         W           S       M
        B L U E   J E W E L S         M
B A B Y       A       A           A
      O       N       N           D
E D W A R D   C R E S T   S L I M
              W
          C O A T O F A R M S
```

HOW WELL DO YOU FOLLOW DIRECTIONS? — Page 2

1. GOODCOMPANY
2. G O O D A C O M P N Y
3. G O O R D A C O M P N Y
4. F O O R D A C O M P N Y
5. F O O R D A C O I M P N Y
6. F O O R D A C O I M N N Y
7. F O O R D A C I O M N N Y
8. F O O M R D A C I O N N Y
9. F O O M R D A C C I O N N Y
10. F O O M R D A C C I O N N
11. F O O M R A D C C I O N N
12. FM RADIO

MAZE — Page 3

BOWL-A-SCORE CHALLENGER — Page 4

STRIKES: 1. awakening; 2. ceaseless; 3. checkered; 4. elevation; 5. furniture; 6. mysteries.

SPARES: (*Other combinatons are possible. Score full credit for them as long as they are correct.*) 1. knew, again; 2. scale, sees; 3. deck, cheer; 4. evil, atone; 5. inure, turf; 6. remiss, yet.

HEXAGON HUNT — Page 6

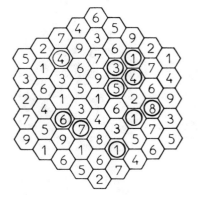

WORD MINE — Page 7

4-letter words: able, alas, babe, bale, ball, balm, base, beam, bell, blab, ease, else, gala, gale, gall, game, glee, lamb, lame, male, mall, meal, saga, sage, sale, same, seal, seam, seem, sell, slab, slag, slam.

Less frequently used 4-letter words: abba, alba, alee, alga, bema, bleb, gamb, lama, mesa, sabe, semé.

5-letter words: abase, amble, bagel, balsa, basal, belle, blame, eagle, easel, gable, gleam, label, lease, legal, llama, sable, small, smell.

Less frequently used 5-letter words: abeam, abele, agama, algae, algal, ameba, babel, balas, belga, blasé, galea, glebe, salal, samba.

CHANGELINGS

Page 7

1. BOLT, boot, foot, fool, WOOL.
2. VOWS, rows, rods, reds, WEDS.
3. HERO, herd, head, bead, beam, TEAM.
4. QUIT, suit, slit, slip, slop, STOP.
5. BEND, lend, land, lane, lame, lamb, LIMB.

(Using the same number of changes, other solutions may be possible for each Changeling.)

TWO-WAY ANAGRAM GAME

Page 8

ACROSS WORDS — DOWN WORDS

Across words: jolly (5); ladder (6); export (6); parcel (6); volt (4); section (7); audit (5); misuse (6); chest (5). Total: 50.

Down words: bungle (6); upset (5); thick (5); relieve (7); once (4); depart (6); flowery (7); iris (4); habit (5). Total: 49. *Combined total:* 99.

SPELLATHON

Page 10

5-letter words: adage, again, agent, chain, chair, chant, china *(dishes)*, chino, conch, conga, dance, hinge, honey, inane, radar, rainy, ranch, range, tenet.

Less frequently used 5-letter words: ancon, anent, chine, conge, conte, genet, naiad, ninon, nonce, riant, tench.

6-letter words: agency, agenda, airing, chance, chancy, change, coning, daring, engage, enrage, gadget, garage, garnet, hangar, hiring, honing, intend, intent, raring, tenant.

Less frequently used 6-letter words: chinch, concha, conine, nagana, nocent, nonage, rancho.

LADDERGRAM

Page 11

P	STRIPE	TRIES	RISE	T
E	LEASES	SALES	LESS	A
A	PARIS	RIPS	SIP	R
C	CASTLE	STALE	SEAL	T
H	HONEST	STONE	NOTE	S

ANACROSTIC WORD LIST

Page 12

A. Bent
B. Right away
C. Arkansas
D. Item
E. News
F. Donald Duck
G. Error
H. Crazier
I. Open-minded
J. Raft
K. At one time
L. Treat
M. Eisenhower
N. Dirt
O. Bring
P. Occasion
Q. Drew
R. Yugoslavia

ANACROSTIC

Page 13

Author: (Robert) Brain
Work: (THE) DECORATED BODY*

"In Egypt . . . beards . . . were worn in graded sizes according to rank, and even women wore artificial, ceremonial beards to mark their status and authority."

From THE DECORATED BODY by Robert Brain. Copyright © 1979 by Robert Brain. Used by permission of the publisher, Harper and Row.

QUOTATION PUZZLES

Page 14

1. It is a lot easier to fall in love than to climb back out of it.
2. One toy that any child can easily operate is a grandparent.

TREE TRIVIA

Page 15

1. By counting the number of rings—a tree produces a new ring of growth cells each year. 2. Fig (*Genesis 3:7*). 3. Canada; 4. a) true; b) false, a stand of Bristlecone pines in California's Inyo National forest are estimated to be 4,600 years old; c) false; d) true; e) false, many wood products are used in plastics manufacturing; 5. Johnny Appleseed; 6. April; 7. a) the redwood or sequoia of California, at 362 ft.; b) the cedars of Lebanon (*I Kings 5:6*); c) cherry; d) chestnut (from the poem "The Village Blacksmith"); e) apple; 8. a; 9. fir, oak, rowan, elm, spruce, tamarack (*others are possible*); 10. "A poem lovely as a tree."

CRYPTOQUIZZES

Page 16

1. buggy, sleigh, wagon, stagecoach, hansom cab, carriage, tandem, buckboard, sulky, chariot; 2. Victorian, French Provincial, Empire, Colonial, Chippendale, Hepplewhite, Early American, Danish Modern; 3. Cuba, Chile, Cyprus, Cameroon, Canada, China, Costa Rica, Colombia, Cape Verde, Chad; 4. Tonto, black mask, silver bullets, "Hi-yo Silver, away!", Texas Ranger, old west, good guys, "Kemo Sabe," caught outlaws.

LOGIC PROBLEM

Page 18

We can identify the five men according to where they live in relation to Tom. Tom lives one floor above Collins (clue 4), two floors above the man who is buying his apartment (clue 1), three floors above the man who is moving (clue 4), and four floors above Will (clue 1). Thus the five live on consecutive floors, with Tom on the highest and Will on the lowest. Will is not buying his apartment or moving, since those decisions have been accounted for by men on other floors. By clue 5, he is not the senior citizen or handicapped, so he is the one who is still undecided. We have accounted for three of the five effects of the conversion: buying, moving, and undecided. By elimination, Tom and Collins must be the handicapped person and the senior citizen, not necessarily respectively. By clue 7, Tom is Mr. Bradford, who is handicapped, and Mr. Collins is the senior citizen. Since Ackley is not Will (clue 6), he must be either the man who is buying his apartment (two floors below Tom's) or the man who is moving from his apartment (three floors below Tom's). If Ackley were the one buying his apartment, then by clue 2, Sam would be Collins, and Roy would live above him. Since that is impossible—Tom lives above Collins—Ackley is moving, Sam is buying, and Roy is Collins. We know Tom is Bradford and Roy is Collins. Sam cannot be Daley (clue 3) or Ackley (clue 2), so he is Erskine. By elimination, then, Will is Daley, who lives on the third floor (clue 3) and Ackley's first name is Val. Since Will lives on the lowest floor, four floors below Tom, the other floors are four, five, six, and seven. In summary:

7th floor: Tom Bradford, handicapped
6th floor: Roy Collins, senior citizen
5th floor: Sam Erskine, buying
4th floor: Val Ackley, moving
3rd floor: Will Daley, undecided

CROSS SUMS HELP: 625

Page 19

CROSS SUMS

Page 19

7	9		7	8			9	7		9	5
3	6		3	1	5		5	9	8	7	3
1	2	4		3	9	5		4	6	1	2
		6	2		6	2	5		9	3	1
9	3		4	2		1	3	9	4		
3	1		1	8	2	4		6	2	3	1
1	2	4	3		4	8	9	7		9	7
	8	5	9	7		1	5		8	2	
8	6	9		5	1	2		8	6		
1	2	6	3		3	1	2		4	7	9
5	1	7	9	2		8	5	9		1	2
3	4		8	1		7	1		3	5	

KRISS KROSS

Page 20

U	S	E			M	R	S			H	A	S	H		T	
	S		I	L	O		T	O	S	C	A		H		R	
S	A	S	S		I		A			S		E	S	P	Y	
W		L		S	E	R	B		S	P	A		I		S	T
I		S	E	A	T	S		A			S		Z		T	
S		A			T		S	I	S		I	D	E	S		
S	P	Y		S	L	A	P	S		T	S	A	R		E	
	A	S	E	A		A		A		A		E		P	I	
	S			C	L	A	S	S		C	A	S	S		I	
	T	A	S	K		H	U	S	K		E	S	S	A	Y	
S	A	M			S	A	N	E			N				E	
P		A	S	S	E	T		T	E	S	T	S			A	R
O		S			O			S		O						
T	A	S	T	Y		P	A	S	S	E		S	N	I	P	S

ARROW MAZE

Page 21

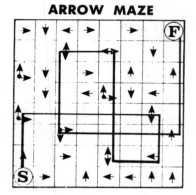

ANACROSTIC WORD LIST

Page 22

A. Brownie
B. Childish
C. Endeavor
D. Rooster
E. Frothier
F. Tarried
G. Humdrum
H. Eggplant
I. Loyalty
J. Affiliate
K. Ultimatum
L. Gentle
M. Hydrant
N. Soothe
O. Offhand
P. Newsletter
Q. Minion
R. Enfold

ANACROSTIC

Page 23

Author: B(ennett) Cerf

Work: THE LAUGH'S ON ME*

"In the days of the silent film, another famous Hollywood dog, Rin-Tin-Tin, received a long and worshipful letter from a youthful admirer. The letter began, 'Dear Mr. Tin.'"

From THE LAUGH'S ON ME by Bennett Cerf. Copyright © 1959 by Bennett Cerf. Used by permission of the publisher, Doubleday and Co., Inc.

WORD ARITHMETIC

Page 24

```
     0 1 2 3 4 5 6 7 8 9
1.   S W A T/O N E/F L Y
2.   S H R I M P/B O A T
3.   B U C K L E/D O W N
4.   L O N G/B R A I D S
```

JIGSAW LOGIC HELP

Page 25

The piece marked by the arrow goes into the upper left-hand corner, so that the filled-in diamond is in the first square on the left in the second row.

JIGSAW LOGIC

Page 25

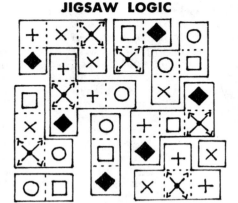

LADDERGRAM

Page 26

R	SPARE	PEAS	SEA	P
I	ALIKE	LAKE	ELK	A
V	RAVENS	SNARE	NEAR	S
E	TEASE	EAST	ATE	S
R	REELS	ELSE	LES	E
B	BONERS	SNORE	ROSE	N
O	GABOR	BRAG	BAR	G
A	BEATS	BETS	TBS.	E
T	SPROUT	POURS	SOUP	R

LOGIC PROBLEM

Page 27

By clue 2, the Carter child is in Ms. Black's class. Also by clue 2, since none of the children is in fourth grade, Ms. Peck cannot teach 1st or 5th grade. Since Holly was in her class last year (clue 3), Ms. Peck cannot teach 3rd; by elimination, Ms. Peck teaches 2nd grade. Ms. Black then teaches 1st grade (clue 2). The second-grader is not Sarah (clue 1), Holly (clue 3), or Michael (clue 4); it is Jon. The 1st grader is not Sarah (clue 1) or Holly (clue 3); it is Michael. Holly is not the 5th grader (clue 3), so Sarah is, and Holly is the 3rd grader. Mr. Turner does not teach 3rd-grader Holly (clue 3), so Ms. King does and, by elimination, Mr. Turner teaches 5th-grader Sarah. Sarah's last name is not Sullivan, Brady (clue 1), or Carter (clue 2); she is Wilson, so 3rd-grader Holly is Sullivan (clue 1). The Carter child, taught by Ms. Black (clue 2), is in 1st grade. By elimination, Jon is Brady. In summary:

Michael Carter, 1st grade, Ms. Black
Jon Brady, 2nd grade, Ms. Peck
Holly Sullivan, 3rd grade, Ms. King
Sarah Wilson, 5th grade, Mr. Turner

LETTER COUNT

Page 28

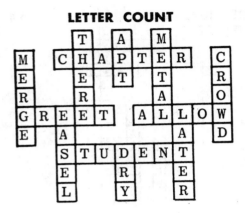

basis (41); 7. uncap (39); 8. block (37); 9. parka (42); 10. speak (40). TOTAL: 405 points. (*Other solutions are possible.*)

QUOTATION PUZZLES

Page 30

1. It requires genius to make the commonplace appear to be new.
2. Friends are that part of the human race with which we can be human.

WORD WHEEL

Page 31

limp, limply, imp, imply, implying, ply, plying, lying, glob, globe, lob, lobe, beg, begone, ego, gone, one, next, extra, trash, rash, ash, ashen, she, hen, end, endow, endowed, owe, owed, wed, wedge, edge, gel.

CRYPTIC MATH

Page 32

By clue 2, E is 2 and K is 4. By clue 4, H is equal to I times I, so I is 3 and H is 9. Clue 3 states that J is 8. The only even number left to be assigned is 6; therefore, by clue 1, D is 6. The numbers left to be assigned are 1, 5, and 7. C is smaller than D (clue 5), so it is either 1 or 5. G is smaller than C (clue 5). Therefore, C is 5 and G is 1. By elimination, F is 7. In summary: C = 5, D = 6, E = 2, F = 7, G = 1, H = 9, I = 3, J = 8, and K = 4.

MOVIE THEME MATCH

Page 32

1. d; 2. e; 3. a; 4. b; 5. c; 6. h; 7. g; 8. f.

BUILD SCORE

Page 33

1. scuba (45); 2. scrub (41); 3. basil (40); 4. skull (45); 5. spade (35); 6.

LADDERGRAM

Page 34

A	ROAST	SORT	ROT	S
S	LISTENS	SILENT	LINES	T
S	AUNTS	TUNA	NAT	U
E	SCARED	CARDS	SCAR	D
M	SCREAM	ACRES	CARS	E
B	BEANS	SANE	SEA	N
L	SHALT	HATS	ASH	T
Y	STRAY	TARS	ART	S

SPELLATHON

Page 35

adage, anger, award, aware, dared, darer, defer, drawn, dried, drier, fewer, forge, frown, grown, organ, radar, range, rarer, rawer, refed, refer, reran, rowed, rower, wager, weird, wired, wirer.

Less frequently used words: arara, dewan, gnawn, rager, rewed, rowan, wried, wrier.

CRYPTOGRAMS

Page 36

1. If your life is an open book, don't bore folks by reading out of it.

2. Today's nostalgia consists of recalling yesterday's prices.

3. Sure, success is sweet, but its secret is sweat.

4. Hockey players really know how to pass the puck.

5. Nostalgia is the file that removes any rough edges from the good old days.

6. It takes both sun and rain to make a wonderful and delightful rainbow.

7. True friendship cannot be purchased at a fair.

8. Measure a person for great substance by the stretch of his imagination.

9. Many relatives attend festive family reunion held in old homestead.

ANACROSTIC WORD LIST Page 38

A. Martian
B. Cut through
C. Curfew
D. Adjusts
E. Rub elbows with
F. Tell-tale
G. Holders
H. Yesterday
I. Ideally
J. Nothing doing
K. Offspring
L. Nail file
M. Elephant Butte
N. Eye shadow
O. Aggregate
P. Raiding

ANACROSTIC Page 39

Author: (Joe) McCarthy
Work: IN ONE EAR*
"An eight-year-old boy was glumly watching a group of fluttering toe dancers in a ballet. He nudged his father and whispered, 'Wouldn't it be easier if they just got taller girls?' "
From IN ONE EAR by Joe McCarthy. Copyright © 1959, 1960, 1961, 1962 by Joe McCarthy. Used by permission of the publisher, Doubleday and Company, Inc.

FOURTH OF JULY MAZE Page 40

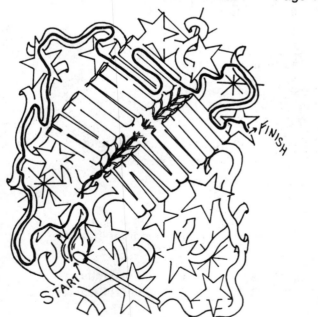

KRISS KROSS Page 41

WORD ARITHMETIC Page 42

```
0 1 2 3 4 5 6 7 8 9
1. H A R M O N I Z E D
2. O L D / A N T I Q U E
3. B E A N / S P R O U T
4. T R A M P O L I N E
```

CROSS SUMS HELP: 3758 Page 43

CROSS SUMS Page 43

CRYPTOQUIZZES Page 44

1. gold, platinum, diamonds, coral, pearls, beads, rubies, turquoise, emeralds, garnets; 2. butchers, bakers, farmers, waiters, waitresses, busboys, produce buyers, short-order cooks, pastry chefs; 3. spies, detectives, undercover agents, counterspies, double agents, operatives, investigators, sleuths, "gumshoes"; 4. crewcut, chignon, "mohawk," pigtails, ponytails, braids, ducktail, "flattop," pompadour, pageboy.

WORD CHARADE — Page 46

```
Y U B R P Y L P
H W A O U (K) P T
U (S)(T)(G) T X F X
T X P O H Y H P
L P L (H) F W F W
H P (L) U H X P U
X L H Y U Y (I) H
Y L T P I W X Y
```

Answer: SKYLIGHT

QUOTATION PUZZLES — Page 47

1. The best time for buying a used car is while it is still new.
2. Civilization is a tug of war between education and catastrophe.

LETTER BANK — Page 48

² L	³ B	⁴ E
² T	³ N	⁴ R
² I	³ V	⁴ O
² Y	³ G	⁴ P

1. glove (11); 2. approve (19); 3. career (16); 4. floor (12); 5. happen (15); 6. knob (7); 7. emerge (15). Bonus word: proverb (26). Total: 121 points.

CHANGELINGS — Page 50

1. SEEK, seed, send, fend, FIND.
2. ROAD, load, loan, loin, JOIN.
3. FUEL, full, fall, tall, talk, TANK.
4. SIPS, saps, sass, mass, mast, MALT.
5. LONG, lone, cone, cane, cape, TAPE.

(Using the same number of changes, other solutions may be possible for each Changeling.)

NUMBER SQUARE — Page 50

77	84	61	68	75
83	65	72	74	71
64	66	73	80	82
70	72	74	81	68
71	78	85	62	69

LADDERGRAM — Page 51

U	DUTIES	DIETS	TIDE	S
M	SWAM	WAS	AS	W
B	BIRDS	RIDS	DRS.	I
R	MARRY	ARMY	RAY	M
E	NEEDS	ENDS	DEN	S
L	SAMUEL	AMUSE	SAME	U
L	SAILED	IDEAS	ADES	I
A	ATLAS	LAST	ALS	T

CRYPTOGRAMS — Page 52

1. The person who attracts good fortune carries with him the magnet of preparation.
2. Most of us find one day of worry is usually more trying than a whole week of work.
3. Habit is the easiest way to be wrong again.
4. In hot weather, the child's sled is not worth "ascent."
5. For any child, the greatest birthday pleasure comes from being "gift-rapt."
6. Farmer's market sign: You know our corn is the freshest because the ears still wiggle.
7. Tears which result from emotion are chemically different from those caused by irritation.
8. Try dealing with the faults of others as gently as with your own.
9. Fishing rods are handy disguises for summer daydreaming.

CROSS SUMS HELP: 97168 — Page 54

CROSS SUMS — Page 54

```
2 1 4   3 7   8 6 5 9
9 8 6   1 2   9 7 1 6 8
    9 7 8   9 2 1   2 6
7 2 8 9   6 8 1   2 7 9
3 1     6 8 7   8 6
9 4   1 5   5 2 7 1 3
  3 8 7 9 6   8 9   2 8
    9 2   1 3 9     5 1
5 1 4   4 2 1   7 4 1 2
8 4   2 1 3   7 9 8
6 2 5 1 3   3 9   6 1 3
  5 9 8 6   4 6   9 2 5
```

KRISS KROSS — Page 55

CRYPTOQUIZZES — Page 56

1. fall, cooler, wings, buffalo, polo, tower, power, pistol, bed, chestnut; 2. saw, scissors, knife, shears, pocket-knife, razor, cleaver, clippers, hacksaw, sickle; 3. Rome, Rio de Janeiro, Reno, Rochester, Richmond, Reading, Rotterdam, Racine, Rangoon, Raleigh; 4. seer, fortuneteller, astrologer, soothsayer, palm reader, forecaster, oracle, diviner, clairvoyant, prognosticator.

NUMBER SQUARE — Page 58

RING AROUND THE SQUARE — Page 59

CRYPTOGRAMS — Page 60

1. The man who loses his head is the last one to miss it.

2. The older I grow, the more I distrust the common idea that age brings us wisdom.

3. Beauty isn't everything, but it is a very good thing to see.

4. Heredity causes a person's parents to wonder a bit about each other.

5. No sense traveling twenty miles to go fishing when you can be as unsuccessful near home.

6. Some friends can be real comforters, while others are wet blankets.

7. Once an opportunity has passed by, it cannot be recaptured.

8. The milk of human kindness will beat cold cream for wrinkles.

9. What a tangled web we can weave when we begin learning to crochet.

10. Love at first sight often deserves a second glance.

11. Word games help eliminate boredom while on long trips.

12. Lovers carve old oak with heart-linked initials.

13. Succulents and cacti create colorful desert oasis.

14. Striking wild meadow lawn eliminates mowing task.

15. Big rockslide blocks mountain road, isolates popular campground.

CRYPTOGRAM HELPS — Page 62

Note: The capital letter is the coded letter; the lower-case letter is the letter that the coded letter represents in the solution.

10. H=n; 11. M=g; 12. Z=d; 13. H=t; 14. F=g; 15. R=c.

KRISS KROSS — Page 63

88

LETTER CHASE — Page 64

1. slow (9); 2. magic (10); 3. level (10); 4. antenna (12); 5. hoax (9); 6. glory (10); 7. remark (11); 8. watch (10); 9. bolt (9); 10. valid (10).
TOTAL: 100 points.

LADDERGRAM — Page 68

B	BORES	ROSE	ORE	S
E	OTHERS	SHORT	ROTS	H
A	CANOE	ONCE	CEN.	O
C	PRICE	RIPE	PIE	R
H	HONEST	STONE	TONS	E

KRISS KROSS — Page 66

LOGIC PROBLEM — Page 67

Mr. Granger is not Carl (clue 1), Earl (clue 3), Adam (clue 6), or Dennis (clue 9), so he is Bob. Carl plays the guitar (clue 1). The piano player is not Adam (clue 2), Earl, or Bob (clue 3), he is Dennis. The fiddler is not Adam or Bob (clue 6), he must be Earl. Since the Texan does not play the piano or fiddle (clue 3), banjo, or drums (clue 8), he must be Carl, the guitar player. Mr. Jackson is not Carl, Dennis, or Earl (clue 3); he is Adam. His home State is not North Carolina (clue 5), Alabama, or Kentucky (clue 2); it is Tennessee. Dennis is not from Alabama or Kentucky (clue 2); he is from North Carolina. Dennis is not Mr. Ingram (clue 5) or Harris (clue 9), so his last name must be Knight. Earl is not Mr. Ingram (clue 6), so he is Mr. Harris and, by elimination, Carl is Mr. Ingram. Earl is not from Alabama (clue 7), so he is from Kentucky, and Bob Granger is, by elimination, from Alabama. Bob does not play the banjo (clue 4), so he plays the drums, and Adam must play the banjo. In summary:

Bob Granger: Alabama, drums
Earl Harris: Kentucky, fiddle
Carl Ingram: Texas, guitar
Adam Jackson: Tennessee, banjo
Dennis Knight: North Carolina, piano

KRISS KROSS — Page 69

DOUBLE-NITIONS — Page 70

1. lot; 2. odd; 3. utter; 4. iris; 5. scale; 6. advance; 7. reflect; 8. meal; 9. season; 10. train; 11. rent; 12. over; 13. note; 14. gray. Name spelled out: Louis Armstrong (*Jazz musician*).

WORD ARITHMETIC — Page 71

```
   0 1 2 3 4 5 6 7 8 9
1. B L A C K S M I T H
2. A B R I D G M E N T
3. G 0/F L Y/A K I T E
4. R I G H T/P L A C E
```

KRISS KROSS
Page 72

```
D E P O S I T       F I S C A L
      U     D I M E     I     E
  T   B     O   P A P E R     N
G R A N T A L O A N   R   C   D
  E   R     E     B   C   U
P A Y   A   I N T H E V A U L T
  S   C C   A     L   A   T   C
Q U A R T E R     A   T   T   A
  R   R E   B A N K E R S   S H
  Y   D U E     C       D   H A
    B   I   R A T E         A C
  M O R T G A G E         C H
  N   N   M C   B R A N C H   E
B O A R D   O E             E C
  N     C U   I   H
C E N T S O N   P   A     B A N K
  Y     U N   T O T A L   A   D
        M I N T   S   F U N D S
```

LADDERGRAM
Page 73

F	FLATS	LAST	ALS	T
I	LASSIE	SALES	LASS	E
N	EVENS	VEES	EVE	S
A	STALE	LETS	ELS	T
L	LESSON	NOSES	ONES	S

FIGGERIT WORD LISTS
Page 74

1. vanish, hesitate, viewpoint, Montana, scarecrow, harmonica, Cousteau, Des Moines, John Doe; 2. telephone, salad, armor, mister, lanes, safer, windows; 3. Rover, women, freeze, heather, final, relatives, allowed; 4. Bob Hope, Sweet, Robin Hood, agreement, Virginia, stammer, at the most; 5. choice, attends, evidence, crayons, parent, history, musical; 6. incline, zenith, tactless, brothers, Oriental, attic, creation; 7. hardship, and so on, infant, Henderson, on the wing, Georgia, hotheaded; 8. consume, gusts, incense, mighty, tights, revolve, shortly; 9. muffle, wholesome, lithe, mosquito, follow-up, missile, shifty.

FIGGERITS
Page 74

1. No one needs a vacation as much as the person who just had one.
2. Man is a plant whose flowers are dreams.
3. We all have more friends than we realize.
4. No matter how bad prose is, it might be verse.
5. To a child, every success is an important one.
6. It's easier to criticize than to be tolerant.
7. He who dares nothing need hope for nothing.
8. Smiles cost nothing, yet give so very much.
9. He who is too full of himself is quite empty.